1/982

How to Program
MICROCOMPUTERS

by

William Barden, Jr.

Howard W. Sams & Co., Inc.
4300 WEST 62ND ST. INDIANAPOLIS, INDIANA 46268 USA

Preface

Computers have evolved dramatically in size over the last 30 years, shrinking from government-funded 20-ton behemoths to a few microprocessor "chips" that can be held in one's hand. Because these chips can be mass produced by new semiconductor fabrication techniques, the cost of the central processing portion of microcomputers is often only tens of dollars. The effect of this size and price reduction is to make microcomputers available to many groups that could not afford them several years ago, and to enable these groups to apply microcomputer concepts to solve problems and perform tasks that previously could not be done by computer. Not only can an electronics engineer use a microcomputer to replace switches and relays in a traffic light controller, but he can now design an inexpensive weather recorder. The same engineer may come home to a hobbyist microcomputer. Chances are, though, he may find that his son is using it to do his homework, or that his wife is using it to plan the nutritional requirements of tomorrow's meals. The computer, in its most recent form, is truly available to everyone.

Computer programming techniques have been removed from the priesthood of computer scientists and put within reach of anyone who has an inexpensive microcomputer. While programming is not as easy as television science-fiction would have us believe, it is not overly difficult either. What this book attempts to do is provide a guidebook to computer programming on the most basic level, machine or assembly-language programming. Here the novice programmer constructs programs of discrete computer instructions that represent the basic instruction set or repertoire of the microprocessor. The instruction set of the microprocessor can be likened to a shop full of woodworking tools. Each tool is used to perform a certain function, e.g., to chisel, to drive nails, or to drill holes. To build a chair or to program a given job many different designs and paths could be used, and many different types of tools could be employed. The purpose of this book is to offer some guidelines on how to assemble that chair without using a screwdriver to chisel away wood or a drill to pound in nails.

While many microprocessors are being employed in industry, the use of three models is widespread. These three are also almost exclusively used in hobbyist microcomputers. The first is the Intel 8080, one of the original microprocessors of the current generation of microprocessors. The other two are also widely used—the Motorola MC-6800 and the MOS Technology MCS6502. This book discusses the architecture and instruction sets of the three models and draws on the similarities between them. In particular, the instruction sets find a great deal of common ground. Each has similar instructions, such as addition, subtraction, and shifting. When programming examples are provided, the general approach to the problem is first treated, and then specific implementation of the problem on each of the three types is illustrated. While this book will not produce a polished programmer, just as one carpentry class does not yield a master craftsman, it should help in producing a chair that can at least be used in the spare bedroom.

The book is divided into four parts. The first, "Basic Concepts," may be scanned by those readers who already know the binary, octal, and hexadecimal number systems, basic operations with binary numbers, basic computer operation, and binary-coded-decimal and ASCII codes. The second, "Microcomputer Architecture and Operation," covers 8080, 6800, and 6502 architecture in the first chapter of Part 2. The many microcomputer addressing modes are covered in the next chapter. Types of memory and stack operation associated with microcomputers are described in the third chapter of this part. Similarities and differences between the instruction sets of the three microprocessors are treated in the next chapter. Input/output (I/O) and interrupt processing are described in the last two chapters of this part.

Part 3, "Assembly Language Programming With Microcomputers," covers the techniques of using the instruction sets of the three microprocessors to perform the functions of moving data, arithmetic operations, double- and multiple-precision, branching, loops, indexing, subroutines, stack operations, table and list processing, bit processing, decimal and floating-point operations, and I/O operations. Examples are provided of the general approach to the problem. For example, there are three or more ways to multiply numbers in microprocessors. These methods are first described without regard to microprocessor, and are then implemented on each of the three microprocessors with illustrations of the actual assembly language code used to perform the function.

The last part of the book provides a number of precanned routines to perform common operations. The reason for this is twofold. The routines provide the reader with a complete model to follow for many of the techniques discussed in the book. In addition, these *are* useful routines that can be used by the reader on his 8080, 6800, or 6502 system, saving him many hours of reinventing the power drill (if the reader will excuse one more reference to the workshop analogy). Both assembly-language and machine code is provided.

Programming in assembly language is enjoyable, it is extremely rewarding, and the resulting programs are at least two orders of magnitude faster in execution than higher-language interpreters. This means that your assembly language programs will run in seconds rather than minutes, and minutes rather than hours. The author hopes that the reader will gain as much pleasure as he has from this type of programming.

WILLIAM BARDEN, JR.

To Clara Barden and William (Blackie) Damp

Contents

PART 3: ASSEMBLY LANGUAGE PROGRAMMING
WITH MICROCOMPUTERS

PART 4: PROGRAMMING ALGORITHMS

UNSPM Single-Precision Multiply for 8080, 6800, 6502
UNSPD Single-Precision Divide for 8080, 6800, 6502
MPADD Multiple-Precision Add for 8080, 6800, 6502
MPSUB Multiple-Precision Subtract for 8080, 6800, 6502
ASBXB ASCII Binary to Binary for 8080, 6800, and 6502
ASOXB ASCII Octal to Binary for 8080
ASDXB ASCII Decimal to Binary for 8080, 6800, 6502
ASHXB ASCII Hexadecimal to Binary for 8080, 6800, 6502
BXASB Binary to ASCII Binary for 8080, 6800, 6502
BXASO Binary to ASCII Octal for 8080
BXASD Binary to ASCII Decimal for 8080, 6800, 6502
BXASH Binary to ASCII Hexadecimal for 8080, 6800, 6502
MVDAT Move Data Subroutine for 8080, 6800, 6502
FILLD Fill Data Subroutine for 8080, 6800, 6502
COMST Compare String Subroutine for 8080, 6800, 6502
SRTAB Search Table Subroutine for 8080, 6800, 6502
RANDM Random Number Generator for 8080, 6800, 6502

Basic Concepts

The Microcomputer Explosion

It's customary in a first chapter such as this to give a history of computers, starting with primitive man's discovery that he had ten digits on his hands, and progressing through the abacus, "Napier's Bones," Jacquard's punched-card equipment, "Babbage's folly," and IBM. The microcomputer is such a recent and important advancement, however, that early computational history really isn't very relevant. Certainly the concepts of number systems, mathematics, and electronics have taken thousands of years to develop. The microcomputer, though, in its first implementation, is just a tyke. It has been with us for only a few years.

The modern digital computer was conceived during World War II. Spurred on by the need for war research and the solution of complex mathematical problems, early machines such as EDVAC (*E*lectronic *D*iscrete *V*ariable *A*utomatic *C*alculator) and ENIAC (*E*lectronic *N*umerical *I*ntegrator *a*nd *C*omputer) were completed shortly after the war. Basic concepts, such as storage of computer instructions inside the computer's memory, and various memory devices were developed in this period.

The size and cost of these primitive computers were instrumental in shaping public stereotypes about computers in general for many years. The ENIAC, for example, used 18,000 vacuum tubes similar to radio-type vacuum tubes, occupied a 30-foot by 50-foot room, and weighed 30 tons. The UNIVAC I, the first commercially available large-scale computer, although cleaner in appearance, was not much of an improvement in size. It was introduced in 1951. During the next twenty years computers began to shrink rapidly in size. Vacuum-tube technology in the early machines gave way to transistor technology, and by the late 1950s computers were being sold that were a factor of ten smaller than their predecessors.

With the development of integrated circuits, another dramatic size reduction appeared. Integrated circuits less than a square inch in size held the equivalent of hundreds of transistors. Computers were now getting down to desk-top size, or at least approaching it. In 1965, Digital Equipment Corporation (DEC) introduced a 12-bit true minicomputer, the PDP-8. The PDP-8, however, sold for about $18,000, which was still out of the range of the average consumer, especially when optional equipment such as printers and magnetic tape recorders were added to the computer to make up a computer system. However, prices *were* coming down. In addition, minicomputers were now much more versatile and faster than earlier machines. Whereas the ENIAC could perform about 5000 additions per second, the PDP-8 could do perhaps 500,000. In place of the patch cords of the ENIAC, the PDP-8 had fairly efficient core memory and the beginnings of powerful user-oriented software programs.

During the next ten years, minicomputers continued to decrease in size and price, with corresponding increases in speed of operation, capabilities, and support software. By the early 1970s, small configurations of minicomputers were actually available for about $5000. Computers such as Data General's Nova, the PDP-8, and Computer Automation's "Naked Mini" series made it possible for a rather affluent experimenter or hobbyist to purchase a minicomputer system for use in his home.

A significant parallel development of integrated circuitry, however, made the home computer a reality. Intel Corporation, a semiconductor manufacturer supplying integrated circuits used in many minicomputers, developed the first microprocessor chip, the Intel 4004, in 1971. Originally intended for use as a "controller" chip, the 4004 implemented a complete cpu (or *c*entral *p*rocessing *u*nit) on a single chip. It was true that a dozen or so other chips were needed to make up a complete computer control system and that only four binary digits could be processed at one time, but the implications of a "computer on a chip" were intriguing.

The following year Intel brought out a much more powerful microprocessor chip, the 8008. It had 48 instructions in its repertoire, was faster than the 4004, and could handle data in slices of 8 binary digits, or one "byte." In addition, the 8008 was competition to minicomputers at the time, since it could replace those minicomputers that were dedicated to simpler tasks. Although initially high in cost, as are the products of many new technologies, prices on the 8008 dropped to the $100 range.

Intel's next answer to the system designer's needs was their 8080 microprocessor chip, again a great advancement over the previous generation. Due to a new fabrication technology, it was faster both from a hardware aspect and the effective number of operations per second, and it had a larger instruction repertoire.

By this time other semiconductor manufacturers were enthusiastically producing microprocessor chip designs of their own. Literally dozens of microprocessors began to appear, either offering new architectures and instruction sets or duplicating another manufacturer's design as a "second source." Motorola Semiconductor's MC6800 microprocessor and MOS Technology's MCS6502 microprocessor became two of the most popular competitors of the 8080. With increasing competition came ever lowering prices, not only for the microprocessor chips themselves, but for support chips and semiconductor memory devices.

Although some early microcomputer manufacturers brought out microcomputers based on Intel's 8008, it remained for Micro Instrumentation and Telemetry Systems (which became MITS) to successfully introduce the first low-cost true "home" computer. The MITS Altair 8800 was brought out in the first part of 1975, and was an overnight success. It offered an 8080-based microcomputer with limited memory, control panel, power supply, and complete packaging for under $500. For the first time, the home computer was within reach of anyone who was interested and could afford the price of a stereo or good-quality camera. MITS soon followed the Altair 8800 with a 6800-based model.

Based on the success of the MITS microcomputers, other manufacturers started producing microcomputers. Some of these were very similar to the MITS design, even to the extent of using the same MITS "bus" structure for their plug-in cards. Others were complete redesigns based on the 8080. Still others used the 6800 or 6502 or other microprocessor chips as a base. In addition to the microcomputers themselves, a large number of support products, such as memories and input/output devices, started being produced. All were priced relatively low in comparison to minicomputer prices.

Currently there are many excellent products being offered at reasonable prices. Basic systems start at several hundred dollars. Options can be added as the budget allows. For the price of a thousand dollars or so, one can have a home computer system equivalent to *or surpassing* the typical minicomputer system of five years ago. Furthermore, prices will continue to drop from year to year as integrated-circuit technology develops and the microprocessor market expands.

What can you do with your system? Hobbyists have used their microcomputers to decode Morse code from amateur radio receivers, to control the heating systems of their homes, to aid them in diet planning, to offer their children programmed instruction or visual games on television terminals, and to plan their stock market purchases. The list of what has been done goes on and on, but the list of what could and will be done by the home computer hobbyist is endless. The use of your hobbyist computer is bounded only by your imagination.

This book will attempt to aid in the pursuit of your personal programming goals by providing a description of the basic concepts involved in microcomputers in Chapters 2 through 5. Part 2 describes microcomputer architecture and operation for those microcomputers based on the 8080, 6800, and 6502 microprocessor chips. It is a prerequisite to the actual programming of the microcomputers. Part 3 offers assembly language programming techniques for the microcomputers described in Part 2. Part 4 provides a number of "canned" programming modules in assembly language that can be taken directly from the section and used in your microcomputer system with little or no modification. Since these represent routines that are used over and over again, they may save the reader from "reinventing the wheel" and let him devote his time and energy to "main line" programming, which is usually much more enjoyable.

In addition to the techniques covered in the book, the reader is urged to read and subscribe to the many hobbyist periodicals devoted to home computing. Many of these provide complete programs or subroutines, in addition to articles on computer hardware and programming.

2

Binary and
Other Number Systems

Somewhere, in a universe parallel to ours, there exists a race identical to the human race except that on each hand there is a thumb and three fingers, making a grand total of eight digits on both their hands. Long ago, the race started becoming civilized and described amounts by holding up the appropriate number of digits. Three horses were represented by three fingers held up, for example, six head of cattle by six fingers, seven gflarks by seven fingers, and so forth.

For a while, herds of gflarks greater than eight were represented by members of the race wiggling their fingers several or many times, depending upon the number. Then, one of the more astute members of this parallel race found that fourteen gflarks could be represented by holding up eight fingers and then by holding up six more fingers. Gradually the race began to develop their number system. When writing was introduced, a type of positional notation was employed. A number like 16 represented one set of eight fingers plus six fingers. The number 35 replaced three sets of eight fingers plus one set of five fingers. A number of 233 was somewhat harder to visualize. It replaced eight sets of eight fingers repeated twice plus three sets of eight fingers plus one set of three fingers. This at first was quite a challenge to the most learned of the race, but through the years they became very accustomed to their way of representing numbers and developed many techniques for working with the number system.

If in this parallel universe eight was used as a base, why not four, two, or even nine (three digits on three hands)? In any of these number systems, it's fairly easy to understand the positional notation, but a little harder to work with it. In our decimal system, the number 1239 actually represents, by convention only,

$$1 \times 10^3 + 2 \times 10^2 + 3 \times 10^1 + 9 \times 10^0 =$$
$$1000 + 200 + 30 + 9 = 1239.$$

Any number to the zeroth power, of course, is equal to one, so that $9 \times 10^0 = 9 \times 1$. The powers of ten increase by one from right to left, so that any size number can be represented. Likewise, so it is in number systems that use different numbers from ten as a *base*. In the parallel universe example, a large herd of gflarks might contain, in their notation, 4577 animals, or

$$4 \times 8^3 + 5 \times 8^2 + 7 \times 8^1 + 7 \times 8^0 \text{ animals.}$$

In our decimal system the above number would correspond to

$$4 \times 512 + 5 \times 64 + 7 \times 8 + 7 = 2431 \text{ gflarks.}$$

For convenience in working with several number systems, the base of the number system is usually written as a subscript to the number, as in 1239_{10} or 4577_8. The former number would be base 10, or decimal, and the latter base 8, or *octal*.

Trying some more examples of different number systems, consider a base of 11. The number $467A_{11}$ would actually represent

$$4 \times 11^3 + 6 \times 11^2 + 7 \times 11^1 + 10 \times 11^0$$

or, in base ten

$$4 \times 1331 + 6 \times 121 + 7 \times 11 + 10 = 6137_{10}.$$

Note that no symbol for the tenth digit of the base eleven number existed. The first ten digits were called 0, 1, 2, 3, 4, 5, 6, 7, 8, and 9, for obvious reasons, but the tenth digit had to be given a name, A. The characters @ or ¢ could have been used just as well.

The most important number system for purposes of this book is base 2, as the reader might suspect. The two digits of the base 2 number system are chosen to be represented by 0 and 1, only because of their familiarity to users of the decimal system. The binary number 10110101_2 represents

$$1 \times 2^7 + 0 \times 2^6 + 1 \times 2^5 + 1 \times 2^4 + 0 \times 2^3$$
$$+ 1 \times 2^2 + 0 \times 2^1 + 1 \times 2^0 =$$
$$128 + 0 + 32 + 16 + 0 + 4 + 0 + 1 = 181_{10}.$$

Unlike the other systems discussed, the value for each positional digit is either the power of the base or zero, so that the binary system is sometimes called a "1-2-4-8" type of code. The first ten decimal digits are represented in binary by

8	4	2	1	Decimal
			0	0
			1	1
		1	0	2
		1	1	3
	1	0	0	4
	1	0	1	5
	1	1	0	6
	1	1	1	7
1	0	0	0	8
1	0	0	1	9
1	0	1	0	10

The powers of two corresponding to the positional notation have been recorded above each binary digit. "Binary digit" has been contracted to the word *bit*. "Four bits" means the same thing as "four binary digits," and a four-bit value would be something like 1010_2 or 1111_2. Other samples of binary values would be the six-bit value 101000_2, converting to

$$1 \times 2^5 + 1 \times 2^3 = 40_{10},$$

and the five-bit binary value of 11111_2, converting to

$$1 \times 2^4 + 1 \times 2^3 + 1 \times 2^2 + 1 \times 2^1 + 1 \times 2^0 =$$
$$16 \quad + \quad 8 \quad + \quad 4 \quad + \quad 2 \quad + \quad 1 \quad = 31_{10}.$$

The last example points out an interesting fact. The largest value that can be held in any *n*-bit binary number is one less than 2^n. For example, in 11111_2, *n* is 5 and 2^5 is 32. One less than 32 is 31, as shown. The maximum value that could be held in an eight-bit binary number is 11111111_2 or $2^8 - 1 = 255$. The maximum value in a 16-bit binary number is $2^{16} - 1$, or 65,535. Eight-bit and 16-bit binary numbers are mentioned because they are widely used in computer equipment.

Why use binary numbers at all in microcomputers? The answer to that lies in the nature of the electronic devices used in microcomputers. It is far easier to implement an "on-off" device, or two-state device, than one that has eight or ten states. Electronic components tend to age, and the more states a device must have, the harder it is to keep the device calibrated. Binary representation will probably be used in microcomputers until the discovery of a natural device that has perfect stability in ten states, can be miniaturized, and uses low power.

Since, for the time being, the reader is inexorably tied to the binary system in microcomputers, it would be nice to find some easier ways to work with it. Rather than laboriously converting from binary representation to decimal by writing down powers of two, a more convenient way is offered. This is the *double-dabble* system, and gets its name from the method of conversion, which involves taking a bit from the left, doubling it, and adding it to the bit to the right (dabble). The binary number 10111_2, for example, can be converted to decimal by taking the leftmost 1, doubling it, adding it to 0, yielding 2. The 2 is then doubled and added to the next bit of 1, yielding 5. The process is repeated until the partial result has been added to the rightmost bit.

$$10111_2:$$
$$1 \times 2 + 0 = 2$$
$$2 \times 2 + 1 = 5$$
$$5 \times 2 + 1 = 11$$
$$11 \times 2 + 1 = 23 \text{ (answer)}$$

$$1010_2:$$
$$1 \times 2 + 0 = 2$$
$$2 \times 2 + 1 = 5$$
$$5 \times 2 + 0 = 10 \text{ (answer)}$$

Fractional representation is also possible in the binary (or other base) system. Rather than calling the point separating the integer from the fraction the decimal point, the point is called, appropriately enough, the binary point. Bits to the right of the binary point represent fractional bits in the orders of $\frac{1}{2}$, $\frac{1}{4}$, $\frac{1}{8}$, $\frac{1}{16}$, and so forth. The mixed binary number of 1010.111, for example, represents the integer 10_{10} plus $\frac{1}{2} + \frac{1}{4} + \frac{1}{8}$ or 10 plus $\frac{7}{8} = 10.875$. Unfortunately, double-dabble doesn't work too well with fractional binary numbers, but the good news is that normally one need not be too concerned with fractions in microcomputers, except when scaling numbers or working with floating-point numbers, both covered in later chapters.

The process of converting from decimal to binary is a little bit more tedious. The decimal number is divided by two and any remainder is saved. The quotient is again divided by two and the remainder saved, and the process continues until the last quotient is divided by two. The remainders, in reverse order, are the binary number. An example should help to clarify this approach. To convert 123_{10} to binary,

$$2 \overline{)123} = 61 \text{ remainder } 1$$
$$2 \overline{)\ 61} = 30 \text{ remainder } 1$$
$$2 \overline{)\ 30} = 15 \text{ remainder } 0$$
$$2 \overline{)\ 15} = 7 \text{ remainder } 1 \qquad 1111011_2 = 123_{10}$$
$$2 \overline{)\ 7} = 3 \text{ remainder } 1$$
$$2 \overline{)\ 3} = 1 \text{ remainder } 1$$
$$2 \overline{)\ 1} = 0 \text{ remainder } 1$$

An alternative method to the division process is the *power-of-two* approach, where the decimal number is "inspected" to find the largest power of two that can be subtracted from it. The process continues until the original decimal number is reduced down to zero.

Meanwhile, back in our alternate universe, the eight-digited race has just entered the microcomputer age and made an amazing discovery. Rather than working with long strings of binary numbers, they have discovered a shorthand notation involving their beloved base eight notation. Taking any three bits at a time from the right of a binary number, they have discovered that conversion to base eight, or octal representation, is very easy to do. Also, reconversion from octal representation to binary is just as simple. The binary number 10110101_2, for instance, is first divided into groups of three bits, starting from the right: 10)110)101. Note that the leftmost group lacks one bit. Each group of three bits is now converted to one of the eight octal digits 0 through 7. Thus binary 10)110)101 becomes 265_8. When 265_8 is compared to 10110101_2, they are both found to equal 181_{10}. Likewise, octal numbers can be easily converted to binary. The octal number 376_8 produces three groups of three binary digits: 11)111)110. The result is the binary number 11111110_2, which, along with 376_8, equals 254_{10}. Octal representation is a convenient way to represent binary numbers. Eight-bit binary values can be represented in three octal digits, and 16-bit binary values can be represented in six octal digits.

Conversion from octal to decimal by the double-dabble method works quite well, but should really be called *octal-dabble*. To convert the octal number 350_8 to decimal, for example,

$$3 \times 8 + 5 = 29$$
$$29 \times 8 + 0 = 232_{10}.$$

Similarly, the conversion from decimal to octal by the technique of division of the base and save the remainder works fine. To convert 2399_{10} to octal,

$$
\begin{array}{lll}
8)\overline{2399} = 299 & \text{remainder 7} \\
8)\ \ \ 299 = \ 37 & \text{remainder 3} & 4537_8 = 2399_{10} \\
8)\ \ \ \ 37 = \ \ 4 & \text{remainder 5} \\
8)\ \ \ \ \ 4 = \ \ 0 & \text{remainder 4}
\end{array}
$$

The three microprocessors discussed in this book all use 8-bit values for operands and lengths of instruction words. (As mentioned previously, an 8-bit binary number is called a "byte.") While octal notation works quite well when speaking of 8-bit values, there is always the problem of the leftmost digit lacking a bit. That is, the leftmost octal digit of an 8-bit value will always be 0, 1, 2, or 3. There is also a problem when discussing two bytes used in a microcomputer: Should the conversion be done on two bytes separately, or on the merged 16-bit value? A two-byte or 16-bit value of 1010110110101110_2 could be represented by 126656_8 or by 255_8 and 256_8. To effect a cleaner shorthand notation, base 16, or *hexadecimal,* is used as an alternative to octal. To convert a binary number to hexadecimal notation, separate the number into groups of four bits, starting at the right. Then change each group of four bits into the corresponding hexadecimal digit. With four bits there can be sixteen combinations of digits. Just as in the case of the base 11 system, the first can be assigned the decimal symbols of 0 through 9, and the remaining six must be assigned some other unique symbols. By convention, the combinations 1010_2, 1011_2, 1100_2, 1101_2, 1110_2, and 1111_2 have been assigned the symbols A, B, C, D, E, and F.

To convert the 6-bit value 1010110110101110_2 into hexadecimal notation, divide the number into groups of four, starting from the right, 1010)1101)1010)1110, and now write down the corresponding hexadecimal digits, $ADAE_{16}$. The double-dabble method works quite well on hexadecimal. Converting,

$$A \times 16^3 + D \times 16^2 + A \times 16^1 + E \times 16^0 =$$
$$10 \times 16^3 + 13 \times 16^2 + 10 \times 16^1 + 14 \times 16^0 =$$
$$10 \times 4096 + 13 \times 256 + 10 \times 16 + 14 \times 1 =$$
$$40960 + 3328 + 160 + 14 = 44,462_{10}.$$

Or, to convert using double-dabble (really a hexa-dabble),

$$10 \times 16 + 13 = 173$$
$$171 \times 16 + 10 = 2778$$
$$2778 \times 16 + 14 = 44,462_{10}.$$

Conversion from a decimal number uses the same divide and save remainders technique as in binary and octal. To convert 4733_{10} to hexadecimal notation,

$$
\begin{array}{llll}
16\overline{)4733} & = 295 & \text{remainder } 13 \\
16\overline{)\ 295} & = \ 18 & \text{remainder } 7 \\
16\overline{)\ \ 18} & = \ \ 1 & \text{remainder } 2 \\
16\overline{)\ \ \ 1} & = \ \ 0 & \text{remainder } 1 \\
\end{array}
\qquad 127D_{16} = 4733_{10}
$$

Fractional representation is also possible in octal or hexadecimal, usually when speaking of floating-point numbers. When octal is used, the digits to the right of the point represent 8^{-1}, 8^{-2}, 8^{-3}, $\ldots$, 8^{-n} weights, or $\frac{1}{8}$, $\frac{1}{64}$, $\frac{1}{512}$, $\frac{1}{4096}$, $\ldots$ The weight must still be multiplied by the value of the octal digit, of course. The octal mixed number 7.153_8 represents the integer 7 plus

$$1 \times \frac{1}{8} + 5 \times \frac{1}{64} + 3 \times \frac{1}{512} = \frac{64}{512} + \frac{40}{512} + \frac{3}{512}$$
$$= \frac{107}{512} = .208 \ldots _{10}.$$

In this case, and in many cases, an exact conversion cannot be made, and some significance is lost in the low-order digits.

The hexadecimal mixed number $A.4F_{16}$ represents the integer 10_{10} plus

$$4 \times \frac{1}{16} + F \times \frac{1}{256} =$$
$$\frac{64}{256} + \frac{15}{256} = \frac{79}{256} = 0.308_{10}.$$

Here the positions to the right of the point represent $\frac{1}{16}$, $\frac{1}{256}$, $\frac{1}{4096}$, and so forth.

Either octal or hexadecimal is a good way to shorten long strings of binary digits. In most cases the notation to be used is dependent on the microcomputer being used. Manufacturers are about equally divided on use of octal or hexadecimal, and it certainly shouldn't be a factor in choosing a microcomputer system. In addition, the reader could do a lot of programming and never encounter fractional representation. After all, what's the meaning of .875 gflark?

Microcomputer Arithmetic Operations

Microcomputer arithmetic, unlike that of larger computer systems, is generally carried out in 8-bit, or one-byte, segments. Now the maximum value possible in n bits is $2^n - 1$, or for this case 255_{10}. This does not mean that the microcomputer is incapable of working with larger numbers, any more than a larger computer working in 16 bits would be limited to $2^{16} - 1$, or $65,535_{10}$. The double-precision and multiple-precision techniques to enable microcomputers to work in larger integer values are covered in Part 3. For the time being, we'll discuss arithmetic in 8-bit segments, since the same rules apply to larger segments, and since this is the actual implementation in all of the microcomputers covered in this book.

The 8-bit segment that we're calling a byte is usually represented in a microcomputer as a *fixed-length* word appearing as a *field* of eight evenly spaced *bit positions*. The bit positions are usually, but not always, numbered 7 through 0 from left to right. Sometimes, because each manufacturer loves to reinvent the wheel, the reverse is true—the bit positions are numbered 0 through 7, left to right. The correct notation will be left to the reader to decide, but in general discussions the former notation will be used, since it corresponds to the powers of two represented by the bit positions.

Bit Position   7   6   5   4   3   2   1   0

The 8 bits in some cases can represent an absolute value of binary 00000000 to 11111111, or 0 through 255_{10}. This is an *unsigned* notation and is used quite frequently in microcomputers to represent un-signed integer values such as counting the number of times a portion of the program is executed, or holding values that can never be negative.

In many cases, however, it is necessary to represent negative values, not only to facilitate microcomputer operations, but because data in the microcomputer emulates the real world. There are certainly negative-valued amounts in the real world, if the author's checking account balance is any indication. Various schemes have been used to represent negative numbers in electronic hardware, but the one in common use in almost all computing systems today, and certainly in use in the microcomputers discussed here, is *two's-complement* notation. In two's-complement notation the *most significant* bit, bit 7, is used to represent a positive or negative sign. If bit 7 is a 0, then the number is a positive number and is represented by the value of bits 6 through 0. Note that the maximum positive number that can now be held in a signed 8-bit value is $2^7 - 1$, or $+127_{10}$.

If the *sign bit,* bit 7, is a 1, then the number represented in bits 6 through 0 is a negative number. However, some adjustment must first be made to that value in bits 6 through 0 to find the actual number represented. To find the actual value represented, take the 8-bit value, change all the 1 bits to 0, change all the 0 bits to 1, and add 1. If, for instance, the 8-bit value is 10110100_2, the sign bit is a 1, indicating a negative number. The number is two's complemented by reversing all bits

$$10110100$$
$$\downarrow \quad change$$
$$01001011$$

and by then adding one to the result

$$01001011$$
$$+1$$
$$\overline{01001100}$$

The seven bits in bit positions 6 through 0 can now be converted to their decimal equivalent of 76, and a minus sign added to yield -76_{10} $= 10110100_2$. Note that the binary addition proceeded just as decimal addition is accomplished. A binary 1 added to a binary 1 produces a 0 and a carry. The carry is added to the next bit position which holds a 1. One and one again are a zero and a carry. The carry added to the next bit of 0 produces a 1 with no carry. The rules for binary addition are straightforward:

0	0	1	1
+0	+1	+0	+1
0	1	1	10

The two's-complement form is a little strange at first, but is very easy to work with. Why use two's complement? Two's complement is used to make the hardware implementation in the microcomputer less complicated as will be demonstrated a little later on in this chapter.

Let's try a few more examples of signed notation. If the binary number is 00011111, then the sign bit is a 0, indicating a positive number. Bits 6 through 0 are 0011111_1, or a decimal 31. The number is decimal +31. If the binary number is 10001000_2, then it is a negative number, as the sign bit is a one. Converting,

$$10001000$$
$$\downarrow \quad change$$
$$01110111$$
$$+1$$
$$\overline{}$$
$$01111000 = 120, \text{ add sign} = -120.$$

The largest positive number in a signed 8-bit value is +127, represented by 01111111_2, but what is the largest negative value? A negative value of −127 sounds suspiciously close. A negative 127 can be found by two's complementing +127 as follows:

$$01111111$$
$$\downarrow \quad change$$
$$10000000$$
$$+1$$
$$\overline{}$$
$$10000001_2 = -127.$$

But what about the signed value of 10000000_2? Two's complementing this value

$$10000000$$
$$\downarrow \quad change$$
$$01111111$$
$$+1$$
$$\overline{}$$
$$10000000$$

produces the original value. GODFREY DANIEL! Since 100000001_2 = −127, 10000000_2 = −127 + (−1) = −128. Thus, while the maximum positive number that can be held in an 8-bit signed number is +127, the maximum negative number that can be held is −128! Two's complementing −128 produced an *overflow* condition in the sign bit position. Overflow is, of course, possible for the result of other additions and subtractions, as will be shown shortly. The following list shows the complete range of numbers that can be held in 8 bits with sign, and two's complement format.

01111111	+127
≈	
01000000	+64
≈	
00000100	+4
00000011	+3
00000010	+2
00000001	+1
00000000	+0
11111111	−1
11111110	−2
11111101	−3
11111100	−4
≈	
11000000	−64
≈	
10000000	−128

The rules for binary addition have already been given. Binary subtraction is similar:

$$
\begin{array}{cccc}
0 & 0 & 1 & 1 \\
-0 & -1 & -0 & -1 \\
\hline
0 & B1 & 1 & 0
\end{array}
$$

A borrow is generated when a binary 1 is subtracted from a zero. The borrow is analogous to the decimal borrow and may be *propagated* along a whole series of bit positions. Although we've seen the rules for binary subtraction, the way numbers are subtracted in microcomputers is by addition of two two's-complement numbers; a subtract instruction actually performs a two's complement of the subtrahend and then adds the two two's-complemented numbers.

Let's see how this works. There are really only four cases to consider in either addition or subtraction. Subtracting a positive number is the same as addition of a negative number, while subtracting a negative number is the same as addition of a positive number. The addend (the number on the bottom) or augend (the number on the top) can be either a positive or negative two's-complement number.

Addition of a positive number to a positive number is shown by addition of 01101111 to 00000011:

01101111	+111
00000011	+ 3
01110010	+114

Note that here it is possible to add three ones in one bit position, producing a one and a carry to the next higher bit position. Overflow occurs when the sum is greater than $+127$. In the overflow case, the sign bit *always* flips to a one, as in the addition of $+64$ to $+64$:

$$
\begin{array}{ll}
01000000 & +64 \\
01000000 & +64 \\
\hline
10000000 & \text{OVERFLOW!}
\end{array}
$$

Addition of a negative number to a positive number (two cases) is shown by the addition of 10000011 to 01111000.

$$
\begin{array}{ll}
01111000 & +120 \\
10000011 & -125 \\
\hline
11111011 & -\ \ 5
\end{array}
$$

Overflow is not possible in this case.

Addition of two negative numbers is shown by the addition of 11111010 to 11110000:

$$
\begin{array}{ll}
11111010 & -\ \ 6 \\
11110000 & -16 \\
\hline
11101010 & -22
\end{array}
$$

Here again overflow is possible when the result exceeds -128_{10}. The addition of -64 and -65, for example, yields

$$
\begin{array}{ll}
11000000 & -64 \\
10111111 & -65 \\
\hline
01111111 & \text{OVERFLOW!}
\end{array}
$$

Because overflow comes up frequently in arithmetic operations in microcomputers, a special *overflow flag* is provided in the arithmetic section of the microprocessor. When arithmetic operations are performed, the flag can be tested to ascertain whether overflow did indeed occur. Overflow is usually, but not always, an error condition. It will be treated again in Part 3.

Another flag that is provided in microcomputers is the carry flag. We've seen how carry from one bit position to another can propagate down two or three or more bit positions. When the carry (or borrow) propagates past the sign bit position it sets a flag in the microcomputer to a one. If no carry is produced in an arithmetic operation, the carry flag is set to a zero. Although a carry is often produced past the sign bit in additions or subtractions, as in

$$
\begin{array}{ll}
11111111 & -1 \\
00000001 & +1 \\
\hline
1 \leftarrow 00000000 & \text{0 with carry out of sign bit}
\end{array}
$$

the main use of the carry flag in microcomputers is in double- and multiple-precision operations, discussed in Part 3. The carry flag was formerly used to test the results of comparisons of two operands (essentially subtractions), subtractions, and additions in many other computers. After the operation, the carry flag could be tested to determine if the first operand was larger or smaller than the second operand. However, in the microcomputers discussed here, arithmetic operations usually set flags indicating that the result is zero, positive, or negative, making testing a great deal more simple. Comparisons of two operands will be discussed in Part 3.

Word should be given here about addition and subtraction of octal and hexadecimal numbers. It will probably be necessary to perform either octal or hexadecimal addition and subtraction depending upon which your microcomputer uses. Octal and hexadecimal addition and subtraction operate in the same manner as decimal operations. When adding two octal or hexadecimal digits, the result is adjusted according to the base. If, for example, the octal digits of 7 and 6 are added, the result is not 13_8, but 15_8. The result must be mentally adjusted by telling oneself "the result is 13 decimal, but that equals octal 15, so I'll write a five and carry to the next higher bit position." Likewise, in subtraction a borrow from the next higher bit position borrows not a decimal 10, but a decimal 8 for octal or 16 for hexadecimal. Subtracting $1F_{16}$ from 21_{16} produces some mental gymnastics such as "F is really 15_{10} from 1, but I must borrow. Borrowing produces 16 plus 1, or 17. Fifteen from 17 is 2, so I'll write that down. The borrow has changed the 2 to 1 and 1 from 1 is 0."

$$\begin{array}{rl} 21 & 33 \text{ decimal} \\ -1F & -31 \text{ decimal} \\ \hline 2 & 2 \end{array}$$

Try a few examples, using the number system you'll be using on your microcomputer. The results can be verified by converting the operands to decimal or binary. You'll be surprised at how rapidly the techniques are acquired even though you don't live in an alternate universe with eight or sixteen digits.

Multiplication and division of binary numbers is probably best handled by converting to decimal first, then doing the operation, and then reconverting to binary. Since all of the microcomputers discussed here do not include a multiply or divide instruction in their repertoire, however, it is necessary to implement a "software" or programmed multiply and divide. These techniques will be covered in Part 3. Multiplication and division of octal and hexadecimal on paper is best left to people who collect miles of string and write crank letters to publishers lamenting the absence of octal and hexadecimal multiply/divide examples.

Addition, subtraction, multiplication, and division are classified as arithmetic operations in microcomputers. Another class of operations is termed "logical" operations. This includes the logical AND, logical OR, and logical XOR.

The logical AND performed on binary numbers has four cases:

$$\begin{array}{cccc} 0 & 0 & 1 & 1 \\ \text{AND } 0 & \text{AND } 1 & \text{AND } 0 & \text{AND } 1 \\ \hline 0 & 0 & 0 & 1 \end{array}$$

When two bits are ANDed, a one is produced if and only if both bits are a one. No carry is ever produced. When an AND is performed on two 8-bit operands, the results are straightforward.

$$\begin{array}{r} 11010110 \\ \text{AND } 01100111 \\ \hline 01000110 \end{array}$$

The logical OR performed on binary numbers produces a one if one *or* both of the operand bits is a one.

$$\begin{array}{cccc} 0 & 0 & 1 & 1 \\ \text{OR } 0 & \text{OR } 1 & \text{OR } 0 & \text{OR } 1 \\ \hline 0 & 1 & 1 & 1 \end{array}$$

When the OR is performed on two 8-bit operands, the results are just as straightforward as the AND.

$$\begin{array}{r} 11010110 \\ \text{OR } 01100111 \\ \hline 11110111 \end{array}$$

The third logical operation, the logical exclusive OR, or XOR, is similar to the OR, but excludes the case of two one-bits combining to produce a one.

$$\begin{array}{cccc} 0 & 0 & 1 & 1 \\ \text{XOR } 0 & \text{XOR } 1 & \text{XOR } 0 & \text{XOR } 1 \\ \hline 0 & 1 & 1 & 0 \end{array}$$

$$\begin{array}{r} 11010110 \\ \text{XOR } 01100111 \\ \hline 10110001 \end{array}$$

The AND and OR operations are frequently used in microcomputers to manipulate data. The XOR is rarely used in comparison. Examples of all three are provided in Part 3, Chapter 21.

Basic Computer Operations

The birth of the computer age with machines similar to ENIAC was prompted by the need to solve complex mathematical problems rapidly—that is, relatively rapidly: hours or days rather than several man-years. The operations that early machines could perform were reduced to simple functions such as add and subtract primarily because of the complexity of the hardware needed to implement these operations. Currently we have somewhat the opposite approach with the introduction and continued development of pocket calculators. Many of these pocket calculators are extremely powerful in the types of operations they perform with a single button push, for example, finding the sine of an angle or a present worth factor. These are functions that are essentially the basic instructions of the calculator themselves and are integrated within the hardware of the device.

Microcomputer functions follow traditional computer functions, rather than implementing dedicated functions. The functions that the 8080, 6800, and 6502 microprocessors perform are basically subsets of functions implemented in large computers such as the IBM 360/370 and the Xerox Sigma 7 series. In many cases, however, the instruction sets of the three microprocessors far outpace the instruction sets of minicomputers.

Microcomputers also emulate the hardware architecture of larger computers and minicomputers. Although generally less sophisticated than the larger machines, they approach or, in some cases, exceed the capabilities of minicomputers in the number of central processing unit registers, stack capability, and addressing ease.

One of the chief differences between microcomputers and their large counterparts is in the size of data values that the former can handle. Microcomputers generally handle data in 8-bit or byte slices, whereas the larger minicomputers usually operate in 16-bit slices, and the "midi" and "maxi" computers work in 32-bit or even larger slices. The second major difference between microcomputers and the larger computers is in speed of operation. Microcomputers operate at much slower clock rates than larger machines. This, coupled with the smaller data slices and consequent need for more processing, result in effective operational rates 10 times slower for microcomputers than for most minicomputers, and even as much as 100 times slower than very large machines.

As the integration technology advances, though, microprocessors will expand to larger data widths, larger instruction sets, and faster speeds. Even now, many minicomputer manufacturers are actually producing a "micro-mini," with an LSI chip implementing the instruction set and architecture of its earlier minicomputers. This process will probably continue until the differences between micros, minis, midis, maxis, and the very large computers become less and less.

Microcomputers based on the 8080, 6800, and 6502 are very similar in architecture, or layout. The central part of the microcomputer is the microprocessor chip itself, which implements the classic cpu, or central processing unit, functions. Those cpu functions are arithmetic operations, timing and control, high-speed storage, and, breaking with traditional minicomputers, stack operations.

The arithmetic, logical, shifting, and other data manipulations are performed in the cpu by an arithmetic and logical unit that essentially performs operations on two 8-bit operands. The results of the operations set various flags, such as the carry and overflow flags previously discussed.

Timing and control functions control the implementation of the instructions in the microcomputer. The implementation of each instruction in the microcomputer, such as an ADD, is composed of several minor parts called *cycles*. Each cycle is made up of clock pulses at some basic clock rate such as 0.5 millionth of a second (500 *nanoseconds* or 0.5 *microsecond*). Instruction implementation can be stopped under certain circumstances.

High-speed storage consists of two or more cpu *registers* which are each capable of holding an 8-bit operand. Since the registers are an integral part of the cpu microprocessor chip, access to them is much faster than to external memory. Typically they hold intermediate results during computation.

Stack operations consist of another register which points to a location in external memory which is the current stack location. The external stack is nothing more than a dedicated set of locations in memory to store temporarily the contents of the registers or other data under certain conditions.

External memory is functionally and physically separate from the cpu. Memory is composed of from 1024 to 65,536 locations. (Each group of 1024 locations is described by the designation *K,* so that 1024 to 65,536 locations can also be called 1K to 64K locations.) Each location is a cell in a semiconductor memory and is 8 bits long. Each memory location has a unique address of a numerical value from 0 to 64K, and is addressed in that fashion, over a set of 16 lines called the *address bus.* Sixteen lines enable 2^{16} or 64K unique addresses. Data is transferred from the cpu to and from memory by an 8-bit *data bus.*

The cpu also interfaces to device controllers which control data transfers to and from input/output devices and the cpu registers. Each input/output device has a unique address and can be addressed by the cpu to transfer data in either direction along the data bus. The address lines also are routed to the device controllers as addresses of both memory locations and I/O devices share the address bus. I/O devices such as Teletypes, paper tape equipment, magnetic tape equipment, and magnetic discs enable the microcomputer to communicate to the external world.

In addition to transfers of data to and from the cpu to the device controllers, data can be transferred from the device controllers directly to and from memory via a *direct memory access* channel, or DMA channel. Whereas the transfers via cpu registers are 8-bit transfers, the DMA permits blocks of data to be transferred without cpu intervention. The device controller accomplishes this by signaling the cpu to stop execution of the current instruction, transfers a byte of data from the block, and then allows the cpu to continue. This interruption, or "cycle stealing," occurs as often as the device controller requires. The data transfer rate depends on the speed of the I/O device itself, which varies from ten bytes per second for Teletypes to 30,000 bytes per second and beyond for disc equipment.

The data represented by the contents of the external memory falls into two groups: instructions to the computer (the program) and data. "Data" represents the data to be processed or constants and variables to be used in processing the data. The various formats of this data will be covered in the next chapter. Instructions to the computer are organized in 8-bit lengths. Depending upon the type of the instruction, the length may be one byte, two bytes, or three bytes long. The convenient instruction lengths are used for obvious reasons, of course. It would not be an easy task to design a machine that worked with 13-bit instruction lengths. (Digital design engineers almost always have two, four, or eight children, never three, five, or seven.)

When an instruction refers to data in external memory, it must reference one of the memory locations by its unique number. In general, since there may be 64K of external memory, 16 bits would be required to contain the memory address. In three-byte instructions, then, two bytes would be devoted to the memory address. An example of this type of instruction would be the 8080 STA instruction which takes the contents of one of the cpu registers, the "A" register (STA is *Store A*), and stores it into the specified memory address. The three bytes for this instruction would look like this:

0 0 1 1 0 0 1 0	Byte 1—Code for STA
XXXXXXXX	Bytes 2 and 3—Memory address
XXXXXXXX	0 through 65,535

In general, two-byte instructions consist of 8 bits of code for the instruction type, and a second 8 bits of operand. The first 8 bits, as in the STA example, specifies an operation code, or op code. Since there may be 256_{10} unique op codes in 8 bits, there is a possibility of up to this number of instruction types, although neither the 8080, 6800, or 6502 chips utilize all 256 codes. The second byte of a two-byte instruction may specify a special form of an external memory address, or data within the instruction itself. The 6800 instruction ANDA #10 performs a logical AND upon the contents of the A cpu register and the second operand within the instruction itself, a decimal 10, and appears as

10000100	Byte 1—Code for AND
00001010	Byte 2—Operand of 10_{10}

The special form of the memory address is discussed in Part 2, which discusses each of the instructions for the 8080, 6800, and 6502.

One-byte instructions have only 8 bits of operation code and no operand. This type of instruction is sometimes called *inherent* or *implied* since the action to be taken by the instruction needs no additional operand or memory address. The 6502 instruction INX, or *Increment X*, takes the contents of one of the cpu registers, the X register, adds one to the contents, and stores the result back into the X register. It looks like this:

11101000	Byte 1—Code for INX

To provide an example of how the microcomputer would run a program, assume that in external memory there is a short program to find the sine of a number. The program is located at memory locations 1000_8 through 1040_8, and consists of instructions to perform the iterative sine calculation *and* data. Program execution starts at location 1000_8, specified by the programmer manually loading the starting address into a cpu register called the *program counter,* or *P counter.* When the *RUN* button is pushed, the microcomputer fetches the instruction from location 1000_8. How does it know that this is an instruction, and not data? It doesn't, and if it erroneously attempts to execute data rather than an instruction, indeterminate results occur, ranging from disappointment to launching 17 ICBMs, depending upon the system involved. Assuming that the starting address was specified correctly, the cpu fetches the first byte from memory. It knows that this must be an op code because the cpu is in the "fetch" portion of the several cycles needed to implement the instruction. The cpu then decodes the op code. If it is a one-byte instruction it takes several more clock cycles to perform the action specified, such as decrementing one of the cpu registers. This is essentially the execution portion of the instruction implementation. If the instruction is a two-byte instruction of the immediate type, such as the AND previously discussed, a request is made to external memory to get the second byte of the instruction. When this has been read in on the next cycle, or set of clock cycles, the cpu uses the operand to finish execution of the instruction. If the instruction is a three-byte instruction, the cpu reads in two more bytes of address over several more clock cycles from external memory. When the two bytes have been read the cpu now has the memory address required and makes a *fourth* memory call to pass one byte of operand to the cpu or from the cpu. In the simplest case this would be storing data from a cpu register into memory or vice versa. In another case, the data byte might be used to perform an addition or logical operation upon the contents of the cpu register.

At the end of instruction execution, which has taken several cycles and from one to four memory *accesses,* the cpu has reset its internal logic to fetch, and is prepared to fetch the next operation code. Somewhere in the execution of the current instruction the cpu has adjusted the P counter from 1000_8 to $100X_8$. If the instruction just executed was a one-, two-, or three-byte instruction, X would be 1, 2, or 3, respectively. The next operation code is then fetched, and the process is repeated for the next instruction. The only exception to this serial execution of variable-length instructions occurs when a jump or branch type of instruction is encountered. If there were no provision for altering the sequence of execution of the program, many recursive or iterative types of programs would not be possible. Even the simplest programming problem must have some way to terminate its operation, and to jump to other parts of the program. A jump or branch jumps to another portion of the same or different program either unconditionally or upon the detection of some condition, as for example overflow. Execution of this type of instruction results in the P counter being loaded by two bytes, specifying the new address for the next instruction to be executed.

When the sine program has been executed and completed, the last instruction might very well be at location 1040_8. This may be a halt type of instruction, which would halt the microcomputer to allow investigation of the result, which could be contained in cpu registers or in some dedicated location in memory. During the course of the program many different types and lengths of instructions would have been executed, including arithmetic, logical, and conditional and unconditional branch operations. Many memory accesses to external memory would have been made by the cpu, both for operation codes and for operands. More detailed descriptions of instruction execution will be given in Part 2, but all microcomputers discussed here operate as in the example given above.

Data Codes Within Microcomputers

The operation codes discussed in the previous chapter are just one type of codes within microcomputers. They are unique codes that are intimately tied to the microprocessor itself. Most other data codes, however, have no relationship to the microcomputer in which they are used. They are codes that have been standardized to represent certain external world actions, such as printing a specific alphanumeric character, or are nonstandard codes peculiar to one I/O device, such as the IBM Selectric typewriter.

The codes discussed in this chapter are the binary-coded-decimal, or bcd, code, the Baudot code, ASCII and EBCDIC code, and the Gray code. All are unrelated to the hardware of the microcomputer, with the exception of the first, the binary-coded-decimal code.

The bcd code is a 4-bit representation of the decimal digits 0 through 9. A 4-bit bcd code is exactly identical with the binary representation, that is

0000	= 0	0110	= 6
0001	= 1	0111	= 7
0010	= 2	1000	= 8
0011	= 3	1001	= 9
0100	= 4		
0101	= 5		

The difference between bcd and binary occurs when more than one decimal digit is to be expressed. When two or more decimal digits are to be expressed, each 4-bit field represents one bcd digit. To find the bcd values for an n-bit number, one starts from the right and divides the string of n bits into groups of four bits. The conversion is then made to decimal digits by considering each group of four bits at a time. The 16-bit number 0001001010010101_2, for example, can be converted to its equivalent bcd value as follows:

$$0001)0010)1001)0101$$
$$1 \qquad 2 \qquad 9 \qquad 5 \quad = 1295_{10}$$

Note that the *binary* number represented by 0001001010010101_2 is *not* 1295_{10}, but 4757_{10}. Note also that a 4-bit bcd number of 1010, 1011, 1100, 1101, 1110, and 1111 is invalid. The value of the 8-bit bcd-encoded number 10001010_2 would be a digit of 8, followed by 1010_2, which has no equivalent bcd value.

Arithmetic manipulations of bcd values are possible. One can add, subtract, multiply, and divide bcd numbers in either software or hardware. As a matter of fact, many early computers operated in bcd format, and numbers were added and subtracted in bcd within the arithmetic units of the cpu. Because storage of binary values is much more efficient than storage of bcd values, the switch was made some time ago to straight binary representation. The maximum possible value in bcd format in 16 bits is 9999_{10}, which is only one-sixth as efficient as binary representation in the same 16 bits.

Consider the addition and subtraction of two bcd values. If a binary arithmetic unit is to properly add two 2-digit bcd values such as 46_{10} and 66_{10}, certain adjustments must be made to the "adder" of the arithmetic unit to enable it to properly add bcd digits. The values 46_{10} and 66_{10} in bcd format would be added as follows in a binary adder:

$$
\begin{array}{r}
01000110 \\
01100110 \\
\hline
10101100
\end{array}
$$

This number is not a valid bcd number as both bcd digits, 1010 and 1100, are invalid. The correct answer should have been

$$
\begin{array}{r}
01000110 \\
01100110 \\
\hline
C \qquad 00010010
\end{array}
$$

where C represents the carry to the next group of bcd digits. What adjustment must be made to the binary result to produce the proper bcd sum? It turns out that if the sum of any group of four bits exceeds 1001_2, or decimal 9, the proper result is obtained by the addition of a decimal 6, or 0110_2, to the 4-bit binary answer. This is done working from right to left with each 4-bit result. For example, in the first 4-bit group of the binary addition 0110_2 must be added to 1100_2, since 1100_2 is greater than 1001_2. When this is done, the result is

$$\begin{array}{r} 1100 \\ 0110 \\ \hline \text{C} \quad 0010 \end{array}$$

which is the proper bcd result of 2 with a carry. When the carry is added to the next group of four bits, the result is 1011_2. Since this is greater than 1001_2, the addition of 0110_2 adjustment is made, producing

$$\begin{array}{r} 1011 \\ 0110 \\ \hline \text{C} \quad 0001 \end{array}$$

which is the proper result, a bcd digit of 1 and a carry. A similar adjustment must be made for bcd subtraction; here a decimal 6 must be subtracted from the result if the result is greater than 1001_2.

The reason that the bcd code is very much tied in with the microcomputer hardware is that in all three microprocessors, the 8080, 6800, and 6502, there is a means to perform bcd addition and, in some cases, subtraction. By setting a flag or by performing a certain instruction the arithmetic unit of the microprocessor acts like a bcd adder. This will be discussed in more detail in Part 3 and referenced to each of the three types of microcomputers.

The bcd code is probably most used in instrumentation such as digital voltmeters, frequency meters, and other digital units where in many cases it is possible to read the values represented under computer control, provided one has the proper interface, of course. Bcd may also be used to represent data in microcomputer memory, but this is a rather inefficient way to hold data, as mentioned earlier.

Another code sometimes used in microcomputer I/O devices is the Baudot code. The Baudot code is used with some older Teletype equipment and a few other manufacturers. Since much of this older equipment is inexpensive the Baudot code is important to those hobbyists who have the equipment and wish to utilize it or to those who want to purchase an inexpensive peripheral device.

The Baudot code is a five-level code, which simply means that five bits are used to represent each character. As we know, five bits can express 32_{10} characters. Since there are 26 alphabetic characters, ten numeric characters, and other special characters, there are obviously not enough bits to provide a unique code for all of the alphanumeric and special characters required. The Teletype and other equipment employing this code utilizes this 5-bit code by using two of the codes to shift the carriage of the unit. One code is used to shift the carriage to upper case, the so-called FIGS (figures) code, and the second code is used to unshift the carriage, the LTRS (letters) code. A third code is used to return the carriage to the beginning of the line (but not to a new line). Another code is used to "line feed," or space the page to the next line.

The remaining codes of the Baudot code are alphabetic, numeric, and special characters, as shown below.

Letters (*LTRS*)		*Figures* (*FIGS*)	
00000	blank (null)	00000	blank (null)
00001	E	00001	3
00010	line feed	00010	line feed
00011	A	00011	-
00100	space	00100	space
00101	S	00101	
00110	I	00110	8
00111	U	00111	7
01000	carriage rtn	01000	carriage rtn
01001	D	01001	$
01010	R	01010	4
01011	J	01011	'
01100	N	01100	,
01101	F	01101	!
01110	C	01110	:
01111	K	01111	(
10000	T	10000	5
10001	Z	10001	"
10010	L	10010	)
10011	W	10011	2
10100	H	10100	#
10101	Y	10101	6
10110	P	10110	0
10111	Q	10111	1
11000	O	11000	9
11001	B	11001	?
11010	G	11010	&
11011	figures	11011	figures
11100	M	11100	.
11101	X	11101	/
11110	V	11110	;
11111	letters	11111	letters

Note that the code seems to follow no logical order. This is true in many codes and makes conversion from one code to another possible only by cross-referencing a character of the source code to a character of the destination code in a table. Here the table might consist of 64 entries representing the binary numbers 000000 through 111111. The most significant bit would correspond to the current state of the carriage shift. A zero would represent LETTERS and a one would denote FIGURES. The remaining five bits would be the five levels of the Baudot code. Each of the 64 entries in the table would hold an 8-bit value corresponding to the destination code. Conversion would then be accomplished by taking the Baudot character to be converted, ORing it with $S00000_2$, where S is a 0 or 1 depending upon the state of the shift, and looking up the corresponding destination code in the table.

The most commonly used code for microcomputers and almost all non-IBM computers is the ASCII code. The ASCII code is a 7-bit code and can therefore represent 128 different alphabetic, numeric, and special characters. ASCII is a "standard" code developed as the American Standard Code for Information Interchange and, much I/O equipment for computers uses this code for communication between the computer and I/O device. The newer Teletype equipment, character printers, line printers, alphanumeric video displays, and most character-oriented microcomputer I/O equipment use ASCII. The ASCII codes from 0000000 to 0011111 represent "control" characters, characters used as special communications characters or to control mechanical features of the I/O device, such as carriage return. The codes from 0100000 through 1011111 represent special characters, numeric characters 0 through 9 and upper-case alphabetic characters, roughly in that order. The remaining codes of 1100000 through 1111111 represent lower-case alphabetic characters and some special characters.

The most commonly used ASCII characters in microcomputers would most certainly include the following:

0000000	NUL	A null character. Produces blank tape on a Teletype.
0001010	LF	Line feed
0001101	CR	Carriage return
0100000	SP	Space or blank
0110000	0	Decimal digits
through		
0111001	9	
1000001	A	Upper-case alphabetic characters
through		
1011010	Z	

Certain other special characters would also be used depending upon the type of task being performed. In many cases only 64 characters are used and the seldom used or unimplemented characters such as lower-case alphabetic characters are discarded. Table 5-1 gives the complete ASCII code in octal notation.

As the story goes, what type of code does a 600-pound gorilla use? Any code he wishes! And so it is with the EBCDIC code used

Table 5-1. Seven-Bit ASCII Code

Octal Code	Char	Octal Code	Char	Octal Code	Char	Octal Code	Char
000	NUL	040	SP	100	@	140	`
001	SOH	041	!	101	A	141	a
002	STX	042	"	102	B	142	b
003	ETX	043	#	103	C	143	c
004	EOT	044	$	104	D	144	d
005	ENQ	045	%	105	E	145	e
006	ACK	046	&	106	F	146	f
007	BEL	047	'	107	G	147	g
010	BS	050	(	110	H	150	h
011	HT	051	)	111	I	151	i
012	LF	052	*	112	J	152	j
013	VT	053	+	113	K	153	k
014	FF	054	,	114	L	154	l
015	CR	055	−	115	M	155	m
016	SO	056	.	116	N	156	n
017	SI	057	/	117	O	157	o
020	DLE	060	0	120	P	160	p
021	DC1	061	1	121	Q	161	q
022	DC2	062	2	122	R	162	r
023	DC3	063	3	123	S	163	s
024	DC4	064	4	124	T	164	t
025	NAK	065	5	125	U	165	u
026	SYN	066	6	126	V	166	v
027	ETB	067	7	127	W	167	w
030	CAN	070	8	130	X	170	x
031	EM	071	9	131	Y	171	y
032	SUB	072	:	132	Z	172	z
033	ESC	073	;	133	[	173	{
034	FS	074	<	134	\	174		
035	GS	075	=	135	]	175	}
036	RS	076	>	136	^	176	~
037	US	077	?	137	—	177	DEL

by IBM Corporation. EBCDIC is *E*xtended *B*inary *C*oded *D*ecimal *I*nterchange *C*ode and has its roots in earlier IBM equipment. It will seldom be seen in microcomputers.

Another code type which is sometimes seen in certain types of I/O equipment is the Gray code. An example of the use of this code would be a simple shaft encoder. The binary representation from 0000 to 1111 can be shown pictorially as in Fig. 5-1A, where dark areas represent a one bit and white areas represent a zero.

By making the dark areas conductive and using a "wiper" to read the four bits, one can get a 4-bit reading of the position of the wiper. If the linear encoding is then wrapped around a shaft, the reading becomes an angular position where each bit represents 360°/16, or 22.5° (Fig. 5-1B).

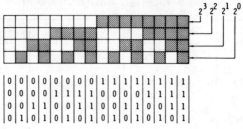

0	0	0	0	0	0	0	0	1	1	1	1	1	1	1	1
0	0	0	0	1	1	1	1	0	0	0	0	1	1	1	1
0	0	1	1	0	0	1	1	0	0	1	1	0	0	1	1
0	1	0	1	0	1	0	1	0	1	0	1	0	1	0	1

(A) Rectangular plot.

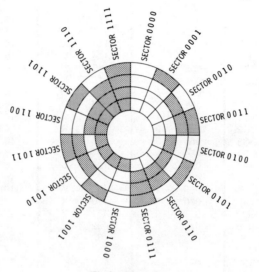

(B) Angular plot.

Fig. 5-1. Shaft encoder.

The problem with this scheme, however, is that there are certain positions of the wiper where alignment becomes critical. If the wiper is slightly misaligned, the reading at the 1000_2 position could easily become 0000_2! This is an error of 50 percent, which is not tolerable even for estimating the federal budget. The use of the Gray code is one way of correcting the problem.

In the Gray code, only one bit at a time changes. It is not possible, then, to be off by greater than one bit's resolution, which is an acceptable error. An example of a reflected Gray code is shown below. It is called a *reflected* Gray code because the rows are symmetrical around the center line, except for the most significant bit.

$$
\begin{array}{rcl}
0000 & = & 0 \\
0001 & = & 1
\end{array}
$$

$$
\begin{array}{rcl}
0011 & = & 2 \\
0010 & = & 3 \\
0110 & = & 4 \\
0111 & = & 5 \\
0101 & = & 6 \\
0100 & = & 7 \\
\hline
1100 & = & 8 \\
1101 & = & 9 \\
1111 & = & 10 \\
1110 & = & 11 \\
\end{array}
$$

etc.

Although other codes will be encountered in microcomputer programming, the codes discussed above are some of the most common. Binary-coded-decimal lends itself fairly well to the 8-bit orientation of microcomputers; two bcd digits can be packed into each 8-bit byte. Baudot is usually right justified in the eight bits with the upper three bits zeros. ASCII is almost suitable for 8-bit bytes—the most significant bit is sometimes used as a check bit, or *parity* bit. With *even parity,* this bit is a one if the total of the other seven bits is odd and a zero if the total is even. *Odd* parity reverses the condition of the parity bit. EBCDIC, when used, fits nicely into the 8 bits. Packing of Gray and other codes depends on the number of bits being handled. The subject of efficient storage of various types of data is covered in Part 3.

PART

2

Microcomputer Architecture and Operation

Microprocessor and Microcomputer Architecture

In spite of what the manufacturer's sales literature says, the 8080, 6800, and 6502 microprocessors are more alike than different. All three are microprocessors fabricated by n-channel MOS technology, which more or less defines the packing density and maximum speed of operation of the LSI device. All three microprocessors have the same number of pins, 40. The fabrication and size of the integrated-circuit package are factors that determine what the architecture of the microprocessor will look like. As a result, the three microprocessors all have 8-bit bidirectional data busses, with larger 16-bit address busses. The remaining pins are divided among the various clock and control signals that are necessary for the microprocessors to communicate with external memory and devices. The speed of the microprocessors is approximately the same, viewed in terms of average instruction execution times. Currently the average instruction will execute in 5 or 6 microseconds, allowing 200,000 or so instructions per second. Even as this book is being written, faster and more compact versions of the three chips are being designed and implemented.

Internally, the microprocessors are also similar. Each has an 8-bit arithmetic and logic unit to perform operations on two 8-bit operands. Each has a set of flags, or condition codes, to record the results of arithmetic operations and define the current system status. Each has logic implemented to allow the cpu to halt processing while external direct memory accesses to external memory are made. Program accessible cpu registers or accumulators are also provided, although the number of each is different. A further similarity is that all three have one-, two-, or three-byte instructions that perform very similar operations, although the actual number of instructions differs. Lastly, all three microprocessors are oriented toward stack operation, and have a stack register pointing to external memory stack areas; in addition the instruction sets and interrupt actions make use of the stack for subroutines and saving the environment. Now let's look at the differences by examining each microprocessor's architecture.

The 8080 architecture is shown in Fig. 6-1. The expected 8-bit data bus is bidirectional and is used to send data to and from external memory and I/O devices, 8 bits at a time. The 16-line address bus addresses external memory only. A control signal is brought up when an I/O device address is present on the *data bus*. Various timing and control signals are sent to or from the cpu. There are external clock signals, an interrupt signal with an acknowledge, a signal to hold processing and an acknowledge, and others.

The arithmetic and logic unit (ALU) is the expected 8 bits wide. It functions as a binary unit or as a bcd adder. A DAA, or *D*ecimal

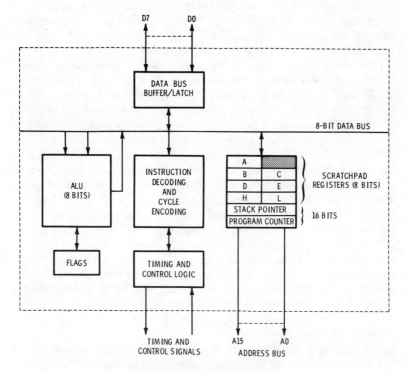

Fig. 6-1. 8080 architecture.

Adjust A, instruction allows the result of a previous addition to be adjusted to a bcd result. There are five flags associated with instruction execution. A zero flag (Z) is set if the result of the instruction is zero. A sign flag (S) is set if the result is negative, and reset if positive. A parity flag (P) is set to provide even parity after the instruction has been executed. A carry flag (CY) is set if a carry or borrow resulted from the high-order bit of the result. An auxiliary carry (AC) is set by a carry out of bit 3 of the result. The AC is used to implement the DAA instruction.

The registers in the cpu are divided into "scratchpad registers," a stack pointer, and a program counter. The scratchpad registers are the accumulators used for holding temporary results. Each is 8 bits wide. The primary accumulator is the A register. Many arithmetic operations can only be performed with the accumulator and another register or memory. The remaining registers are divided into three register pairs: B and C, D and E, and H and L. The H (high) and L (low) registers are used to address memory for certain types of instructions. Taken together, they hold a 16-bit memory address. The original 8008 microprocessor could address memory *only* through these registers, and the 8080 is *downwards compatible* to include the 8008 instruction set as a subset. The other two register pairs may be used for temporary storage or to hold a memory address to address memory, similar to the H and L registers.

The stack pointer is a 16-bit register which is accessible to the programmer. It holds a memory address which defines the current stack area. It may be adjusted by the program or automatically as the stack is used for storage in subroutines or interrupts. The program counter is the normal 16-bit register which controls program sequence.

Microcomputers built around the 8080 microprocessor are exemplified by the MITS Altair 8800 and the IMSAI 8080. Each is basically a box containing power supply, chassis, and front control panel with indicator lights and switches. The front control panel allows a program to be manually entered and executed. Along the length of the chassis, a bus of one-hundred wires is run. Many of the signals on the bus correspond logically to the signals coming out of the 8080 microprocessor, while others are signals generated by additional logic in the microcomputer. Various printed-circuit modules plug into connectors which are connected to the bus. The main module is the cpu module, which contains the 8080 microprocessor chip and other necessary logic. The 8080 requires more supplemental logic than the 6800 and 6502, and so the cpu board contains clock circuitry and decoding logic.

Memory modules consist of RAM (*random access memory*) and the associated circuitry to decode the memory address for the module and to interface to the cpu. Memory module sizes of 4K, 8K, and now 16K are common. Additional modules may contain PROM (*programmable read-only* memory) set up in similar fashion.

In addition to the cpu and memory modules, modules are available for various modes of I/O (serial, parallel) and for different types of I/O devices. The basic microcomputer probably contains a cpu board and some minimum RAM memory, but may be expanded to many more memory and device interfaces by adding additional plug-in modules.

The 6800 microprocessor and microcomputers built around the 6800 take a somewhat different approach. The 6800 microprocessor is shown in Fig. 6-2. Again, there is an 8-bit data bus, which is used to transfer data to and from the cpu registers, and a 16-line address bus. The address bus in this case, however, is used to address both memory and I/O devices. There are no separate I/O instructions. An I/O device is addressed in the same way that a memory address is specified, by a 16-bit address that is present on the address bus. This means that not all of the 64K addresses available can be external memory; at least a small block must be reserved for I/O device addresses.

Internally, the ALU is 8 bits wide and operates in binary mode or, by a special DAA instruction, in bcd addition mode. Flags affected by instruction execution are the H, I, N, Z, V, and C flags. Flag H

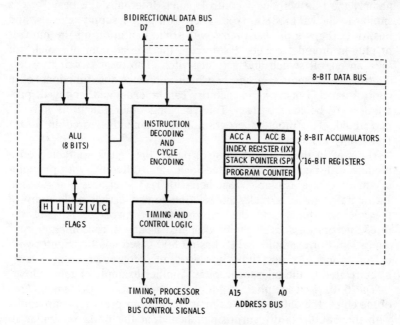

Fig. 6-2. MC6800 architecture.

is a "half-carry" and is used for bcd addition. Flag I is the interrupt mask used to enable or disable external interrupts. If the flag is set, an external interrupt is not recognized by the microprocessor. Flag N is a negative flag, set whenever the result of an instruction execution is negative, and reset if the result is positive. Flag Z is similarly used for a zero result. Flag V is an overflow flag, set if arithmetic overflow occurred in the result. Flag C is the main carry flag.

There are two accumulators in the 6800, designated accumulator A and accumulator B, each 8 bits in length. All instructions can operate on data in either accumulator in general. The third register in the cpu is a 16-bit index register, used in computing the memory address. Memory may be addressed by direct means, where the memory address is specified in the instruction itself, or the index register may contain the necessary memory address. (Memory addressing is further explained in Chapter 7.) A 16-bit stack pointer defines the memory stack in the same fashion as the 8080 stack. Here again the stack is used for subroutine storage and interrupt storage of the environment. The last cpu register is a 16-bit program counter.

Microcomputers built around the 6800 are best illustrated by the Southwest Technical Products 6800 or Sphere 300 series. These microcomputers illustrate another type of construction philosophy, namely the box without a control panel. Internally the basic box is similar to the MITS 8800 type. There is a power supply, chassis, and bus, or perhaps a *mother board* with some limitation on the number of plug-in module sockets. Externally, there is no control panel, but only an on/off switch and a reset switch. The reset switch transfers control to a *monitor program* which simulates the functions of a control panel. Locations in memory can be examined, changed, programs may be loaded from Teletype, and other functions may be performed. The monitor program is permanently stored in ROM (read-only memory).

Here, as in the box with control panel, the cpu is contained on a module with necessary associated logic, and different types of memory modules are available, together with I/O interfaces and devices. Incidentally, there is really no relation to the design philosophy of the microcomputer and the microprocessor involved. Any of the three microprocessors might be designed in any microcomputer configuration. For example, MITS has a 6800-based microcomputer with a front panel. At this time, however, microcomputer designs *seem* to be related to the microprocessor. Another example of this follows.

The 6502 is a member of MOS Technology's 650X family. One of the chips, the 6501, is *pin* compatible, but not program compatible, with the 6800. Hardly surprising, then, that the 6502 is similar to the 6800.

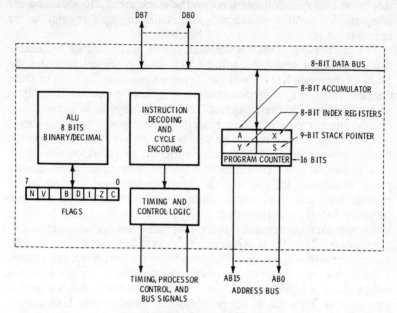

Fig. 6-3. MCS6502 architecture.

As Fig. 6-3 shows, there are the usual 8-bit data and 16-bit address busses. As in the case of the 6800, there are no separate I/O instructions, and I/O addresses are sent to the I/O device controllers along the address bus. The ALU is an 8-bit ALU with decimal mode capability. There are seven flags associated with the ALU and control circuitry of the microprocessor. Flags N, V, Z, and C are negative, overflow, zero, and carry flags, respectively, and are set or reset on the proper condition after instruction execution. The B flag is set after a special instruction called BRK is executed. The BRK instruction provides a software interrupt. An I flag is used as in the 6800, to enable or disable external interrupts. The last flag, the D flag, sets "decimal mode," which enables the ALU to do bcd arithmetic.

Rather than two accumulators as in the 6800, the 6502 has only one accumulator and two index registers. The accumulator, of course, is 8 bits in length, but each index register is also 8 bits long. This means that each index register cannot hold a complete memory address. Use of the index register is still almost as convenient, as is demonstrated in Chapter 16. The stack register in the 6502 is also 8 bits long. The cpu appends a higher-order bit to make a nine-bit value. This means that the stack area is located in external memory locations 100000000_2 through 111111111_2. Although at first glance this imposes a questionable limit on the stack area, 256 locations are adequate for most applications. The remaining cpu register is the redoubtable program counter, 16 bits long.

The third type of microcomputer design is illustrated by microcomputers on a board using the 6502. Two of these types are the MOS Technology KIM-1 and the Apple I Computer. In both of these designs, the 6502 microprocessor bus is kept more or less intact without adding additional signals. The microcomputer is a completely functioning microcomputer on a board, without power supply, chassis, or control panel. Here, as in the box without control panel, the microcomputer contains a monitor program in ROM, which serves as a means to enter programs, modify locations, and other control panel functions. In addition, a complete interface for an audio cassette tape unit is provided, along with on-board RAM memory. In the KIM-1, a hexadecimal keyboard is built on the board to allow the user to manually enter programs and as an interface to the monitor. The Apple requires an external keyboard, but provides a complete television interface which can be used on home televisions.

In both cases, the manufacturer has provided a complete microcomputer on a board, stressing not the expandability, but the usefulness of it as it stands, although additional memory and I/O devices may be added.

Microcomputer Addressing Modes

Many programmers, the author suspects, are waiting for that *Star Trek* rerun in which the U.S.S. *Enterprise* is engaged in hot combat with the Klingons. Heavy damage is sustained by the *Enterprise,* and Damage Control reports that one of the primary battle computers has had a portion of the battle program clobbered. A quick fix is possible, but Scotty is bemused. "Let's see, is that instruction an inherent, Z page relative, or immediate? *Occh!* These computers—there's no standardization!" This appears to be the condition with microcomputer instruction sets and addressing modes—every manufacturer implements their instructions a slightly different way and names their addressing schemes differently. At first glance there seems to be no commonality, but upon further investigation the similarities become apparent.

Why have different addressing modes at all? The reason for this is primarily that the cpu can be told in one byte to perform instruction *n,* but that it takes three bytes for the next instruction. To save memory storage and to decrease execution times, a number of addressing modes are implemented in all three microprocessors and in the resulting microcomputers which are built around them.

One of the simplest addressing modes is what Intel calls *one-byte,* Motorola calls *inherent,* and MOS Technology calls *accumulator* or *implied.* They all amount to the same thing—a one-byte instruction in which the cpu makes only one memory access, to fetch the one-byte operation code itself. Some examples of this type of instruction follow. The 8080 instruction ANA R takes the contents of register R and the contents of register A, ANDs the two operands, and puts the result in the A register. Note that the two operands were already in two cpu registers, and no memory access had to be made to fetch one or two operands. The 8080 instruction CMC complements the C, or carry, flag. Both instructions are one byte long.

$$\text{ANA B} = 10100000$$
$$\text{CMC} = 00111111$$

There are, however, 8080 instructions that are one byte long that result in further memory accesses; these are discussed under indexing. The 6800 instruction ASL, or arithmetic shift left, is another instruction of this type when an accumulator is specified. ASL A shifts the contents of the A accumulator left into the A accumulator and the carry.

$$\text{ASLA} = 01001000$$

Likewise, the 6502 instruction INY bumps the contents of the Y accumulator by one.

$$\text{INY} = 11001000$$

In all cases for instructions of this type there is enough information in the operation code of the instruction itself to perform the operation, and no additional memory accesses have to be made.

A second type of addressing mode which is common to all three microprocessors is the *immediate* type of addressing. Here, the operand is contained in byte 2 of the instruction itself or, if 16 bits are required, in bytes 2 and 3 of the instruction. Hence, one memory access is made for the operation code of the instruction, and one or two additional memory accesses are made for the additional bytes in the instruction which specify the operand. An 8080 example of this type of addressing is the SUI DATA instruction. This instruction takes the one-byte value DATA from byte 2 of the instruction, subtracts it from the A register, and places the result in the A register. Another immediate 8080 instruction is the LXI RP, DATA instruction (load register pair immediate) which takes the value DATA from bytes 2 and 3 of the instruction and loads it into the specified register pair.

| SUI 15 | = 11010110 | Byte 1 | Op code |
| | 00001111 | Byte 2 | 15_{10} |

LXI B, 0260	= 00000001	Byte 1	Op code
	00000100	Byte 2	} 260_{10}
	00000001	Byte 3	

The 6800 instruction ANDB #23 is another instruction of this type. It ANDs the contents of the B accumulator with 23_{10} and places the result in the B accumulator.

```
ANDB  #23  =  11000100  Byte 1  Op code
              00010111  Byte 2  $23_{10}$
```

An equivalent 6502 instruction is the AND #23, which performs the same operation on the single 6502 accumulator.

```
AND  #23  =  00101001  Byte 1  Op code
             00010111  Byte 2  $23_{10}$
```

All instructions of this type are two or three bytes long (two bytes only on the 6502) and require two or three memory accesses.

The third type of memory addressing concerns an instruction in which a memory address is specified in the instruction. This may be an instruction to load data into a register, to store data from a register, to perform an operation with an operand from memory, or to jump to a specified memory address. Examples of this type of addressing in the 8080 are the STA and LDA instructions, which store and load an 8-bit operand into memory and the A register, respectively, and the JMP instruction, which causes a branch unconditionally to the specified memory address. The first two instructions are called "direct" by Intel, and the third is called "indirect," but in all the second and third bytes specify a 16-bit memory address.

```
STA  100  =  00110010  Byte 1  Op code
             01100100  Byte 2  ⎫
             00000000  Byte 3  ⎭ Memory address

LDA  100  =  00111010  Byte 1  Op code
             01100100  Byte 2  ⎫
             00000000  Byte 3  ⎭ Memory address

JMP  100  =  11000011  Byte 1  Op code
             01100100  Byte 2  ⎫
             00000000  Byte 3  ⎭ Memory address
```

In both the 6800 and the 6502 either an 8-bit or 16-bit memory address may be specified. If the address is 8 bits, the memory location referred to is in the first 256 locations of memory, designated the *zero page*. If a 16-bit memory address is specified, then any of 64K memory locations can be specified. Motorola calls the 8-bit memory address instruction "direct," and the 16-bit memory address "extended"; MOS Technology calls the 8-bit type "zero page" and the 16-bit type "absolute." In addition, the 6502 JMP type instructions are designated "indirect." Examples of 6800 instructions of this type are the LDX 100 and the LDX 3000. Both of these load the index register with the 8-bit value found in a specified memory location. The first location can be resolved in one byte (page zero) while the next location takes two bytes.

```
LDX  100  =  11011110   Byte 1   Op code
             01100100   Byte 2   8-bit memory address
LDX  3000 =  11111110   Byte 1   Op code
             00001011   Byte 2  ⎱
             10111000   Byte 3  ⎰ 16-bit memory address
```

A similar example in the 6502 is the JMP instruction, which always appears as a three-byte instruction:

```
JMP  3000 =  01001100   Byte 1   Op code
             10111000   Byte 2  ⎱
             00001011   Byte 3  ⎰ 16-bit memory address
```

The number of memory accesses in this type of instruction is variable. If a JMP is performed, only three memory accesses are necessary, to pick up the three bytes of the instruction. A two-byte page zero instruction would require three memory accesses, while a three-byte memory reference would require four memory accesses, three for the instruction and one for the data.

The fourth type of addressing is not present in any form in the 8080. The 6800 and 6502 both call this addressing mode *relative,* and this is also the name that many minicomputers use. Relative addressing computes the *effective address* by taking the contents of the program counter, which points to the current instruction, and adding a one-byte displacement value to it to compute the new memory address. Since the one-byte value is an 8-bit signed displacement, the effective address is $(PC)-128$ to $(PC)+127$, defining an area of 256 locations around the current setting of the program counter. This area is sometimes known as the *floating page,* since it floats relative to the program counter. Both the 6800 and 6502 use the relative instruction type for only one set of instructions, the conditional branches. Therefore, if the conditional branch condition is met, the program can jump or branch anywhere within the floating page. This is really not too much of a hindrance, since in many cases the next instruction will be somewhere within that area. The 6800 instruction BVS, Branch on Overflow Set, and the 6502 instruction BPL, Branch on Plus, are examples of instructions using this addressing mode. If the conditional branch were at location 1000_8, the program counter would be set to point to the next instruction, at 1002_8. If a branch was to be made to location 1100_8, 64 locations away from the conditional branch, then the instructions would appear as

```
6800 BVS =  00101001   Byte 1   Op code
            00111110   Byte 2   +62₁₀
6502 BPL =  00010000   Byte 1   Op code
            00111110   Byte 2   +62₁₀
```

Branches back from the current instruction would be handled in the same fashion, except that the second byte of the instruction would be a negative value.

The next type of addressing mode is the *indexed* mode. An index register is usually a cpu register that holds an index value which is used to compute the effective address of the instruction. In the case of the 6800, this index register is 16 bits long. The 6502 has two registers that are 8 bits long. The 8080 has the register pairs B, C; D, E; and H, L, each pair being 16 bits long.

Let's take the 8080 case first. There are some who would call this mode of operation in the 8080 an indirect mode rather than indexed mode, but since the effective address is computed by use of a cpu register, the point could be argued. In any case, one of the three sets of register pairs points to the memory location to be used. The original (in the 8008) data pointer was the H,L register set, which was used to make all memory references. Therefore, there are instructions like the one-byte MOV M,R which *moves* an 8-bit byte from a cpu register to the memory address pointed to by the H,L registers. If the H and L registers contained 1000_8, for example, the MOV M,B instruction would move the contents of the D register to memory location 1000_8.

$$\text{MOV M,D} = 01110010$$

Likewise, the 8008-compatible instruction SUB M, subtract memory from A, would subtract the contents of the memory location pointed to by the H and L registers from the accumulator. With the 8080, however, the B,C and D,E register pairs were also given the capability to be used as data pointers or index registers. The STAX B, STAX D, LDAX B, and LDAX D instructions in the 8080 store the contents of the A register into the location pointed to by register pair B,C or D,E or load the A register in the same fashion. Although Intel calls these instructions *indirect,* the suffix X has been used to denote indexing. Of instructions using either of the three register pairs, the instructions using H and L are most common in the 8080.

The 6800 uses its one index register to point to data just as in the 8080 case. In addition, however, the second byte of a two-byte indexed instruction contains a displacement value. The displacement value is an unsigned value of 0 through 255, which is added to the contents of the index register to compute the effective address. Suppose that the 6800 instruction ADDA 20,X were to be executed, an add to the A accumulator with indexing. If the index register contained 1000_{16}, then the effective address would be computed as

(X Register)	$= 1000_{16}$
(Displacement)	$= 14_{16}$
(Effective address)	$= 1014_{16}$

The ADDA 20,X instruction would be present as

$$\text{ADDA} \quad 20,X = \begin{array}{lll} 10101011 & \text{Byte 1} & \text{Op code} \\ 00010100 & \text{Byte 2} & 20_{10} \end{array}$$

The 6502 uses indexing in identical fashion. The 6502 Z Page X and Z Page Y addressing modes are nothing more than using one of the two index registers, X or Y, and the displacement in the second byte of the instruction. The instructions LDX 100,Y and LDY 100,X are Z Page Y and Z Page X types, that compute the effective address by adding the displacement of 100_{10} to the contents of either the X or Y index registers, the same as in the 6800, except that the index registers are 8 bits long. In two other modes of addressing, *ABS X* and *ABS Y* (*Ooch!* Captain Kirk, I still can't find the right patch for the battle computer!), the displacement value is two bytes long. The effective address is computed exactly the same way, by adding the displacement value to the contents of one of the index registers. The 6502 instructions SBC 1000,X and SBC 1000,Y, for example, produce a two-byte displacement as follows:

$$\text{SBC} \quad 1000,X = \begin{array}{lll} 11111101 & \text{Byte 1} & \text{Op code} \\ 11101000 & \text{Byte 2} \rbrace & \text{Displace-} \\ 00000011 & \text{Byte 3} \rbrace & \text{ment} \end{array}$$

$$\text{SBC} \quad 1000,Y \quad \begin{array}{lll} 11111001 & \text{Byte 1} & \text{Op code} \\ 11101000 & \text{Byte 2} \rbrace & \text{Displace-} \\ 00000011 & \text{Byte 3} \rbrace & \text{ment} \end{array}$$

There are two more addressing modes unique to the 6502, *indirect indexed X and indirect indexed Y*. In the former, the effective address is obtained by adding the contents of the X index register to the second byte of the instruction, which holds the displacement value as before. The result points to a page 0 location whose *contents* point to another location to be used as the actual location in the instruction. The page 0 location considered is actually two consecutive locations, treated as a 16-bit *indirect* address. In the second, the indirect address from page 0 is picked up first and *then* the contents of the *Y* index register are added to the indirect address to determine the effective address. Indexed indirect *X* is *pre-indexing* while indirect indexed *Y* is *post-indexing*. Examples and use of this will be given in the following chapters.

All addressing in the 8080, 6800, and 6502 fall in the six categories above. While the addressing modes may be confusing at first, use of them becomes very automatic with some practical experience in programming a particular microcomputer. This will be especially true if the reader is using an assembler program to assemble his *symbolic* program, rather than hand assembling code in *machine language.*

Both are proper ways to proceed, but the assembler will automatically impose the proper addressing modes in the instructions and provide diagnostic messages when addressing mode errors are made. The use of the modes in instruction groups is discussed in Chapter 9, where a cross reference of instruction types and addressing modes is provided.

Microcomputer Memory and Stack Operation

With the advent of inexpensive microprocessors came a parallel development of inexpensive memory that was just as significant. Not very long ago one of the primary costs of a computer system or minicomputer system was the core memory portion. As a result many systems were purchased for applications with just enough memory to squeeze in the required programs. (One of the basic axioms in system design, of course, is that the required applications programs take up 1K more than the memory available. The author has never seen this rule violated. The result has been either the purchase of additional memory or trimming the existing programs to fit by eliminating redundant code and other methods similar to the truncation algorithm of Procrustes.) Today, however, semiconductor memory costs continue to rapidly fall. The average price per bit of memory at this writing is less than $\frac{1}{3}$ of a cent. In addition, inexpensive secondary memories, such as holographic, bubble, and charge-coupled device (CCD) memories, are being developed or are available that will reduce the costs of secondary storage significantly.

The result of inexpensive memory development has many implications. Newer microprocessors will have expanded addressing capability, for example. Expansion beyond the 64K addressing range of the 8080, 6800, and 6502 is possible now, but involves switching memory banks by special instructions and is not an inherent feature of the microprocessor. Another implication is that the hobbyist will be able to concentrate upon writing applications programs without too much regard to making his code space-efficient, that is, taking up as little memory as possible. The hobbyist will soon be able to afford enough memory to fill his microcomputer to the 64K limit. Let's take a look at some of the various configurations of microcomputer memories in the current 8080, 6800, and 6502 microcomputers and see how they are laid out and what the addressing restrictions are.

Memory can basically be divided into read-and-write random access memories (RAM), dedicated read-only memory with manufacturers' programs "burned into" the memory (PROM or ROM), and erasable programmable read-only memory, which the user can program and reprogram (EPROM). All must fit into the 64K addresses of the microcomputer. In addition, in the 6800 and 6502 a small block of memory addresses must be reserved for I/O device addresses which are addressed over the address bus in identical fashion with memory.

If programs such as BASIC are purchased from the manufacturer in PROM, then they occupy a certain segment of the 64K addresses. This area becomes inaccessible to the user of the microcomputer for his own storage. Typically, 1K to 8K blocks of PROM might be used for dedicated programs such as *monitors* and *interpreters.*

The popular EPROM 2708 memory is a PROM which can be programmed by the user by a *PROM programmer.* At any time the EPROM can be erased by exposure to ultraviolet light and can then be reprogrammed. Each 2708 is 1K bytes in size and would therefore reduce the 64K addresses by that amount.

This leaves the remaining area to be divided into RAM storage, and in the case of the 6800 and 6502, I/O device addresses. In the 8080 up to 256 I/O device addresses are possible by use of the IN and OUT instructions which have the following instruction format:

$$\begin{array}{lll} \text{IN} & = 1\,1\,0\,1\,1\,0\,1\,1 & \text{Op code} \\ & \text{XXXXXXXX} & \text{Device address} \end{array}$$

$$\begin{array}{lll} \text{OUT} & = 1\,1\,0\,1\,0\,0\,1\,1 & \text{Op code} \\ & \text{XXXXXXXX} & \text{Device address} \end{array}$$

The second byte of the instruction specifies the device address, which can be 0 through 255_{10}. In the 6800 and 6502 an I/O device is addressed by a memory reference instructions such as a LDAA in the 6800 or STA in the 6502:

$$\begin{array}{lll} \text{LDAA} & = 1\,0\,1\,1\,0\,1\,1\,0 & \text{Op code} \\ & \text{XXXXXXXX} & \text{I/O device address} \\ & \text{XXXXXXXX} & \end{array}$$

$$\begin{array}{lll} \text{STA} & = 1\,0\,0\,0\,1\,1\,0\,1 & \text{Op code} \\ & \text{XXXXXXXX} & \text{I/O device address} \\ & \text{XXXXXXXX} & \end{array}$$

In the LDAA case the I/O device address is sent out over the 16 address lines, recognized as the proper I/O device address by the I/O device controller, and an 8-bit data byte is sent from the I/O device to the A accumulator. In the STA case an 8-bit data byte is sent across the data bus and *strobed* into the I/O device controller's register when it recognizes the device address on the 16 address lines. When a block of addresses must be dedicated to I/O devices in this fashion, the block is usually 1K or so long to simplify address decoding. This means that there is 1K of memory addresses that must be used for the I/O devices in the system and cannot, of course, be used for any type of memory.

After the PROM, EPROM, and I/O device addresses have been allocated, the remaining memory addresses may be used for RAM storage. In the 8080, assignment of RAM, PROM, and EPROM addresses is not too important. It is convenient to group RAM memory into one contiguous block, say location 0 through location 17777_8 and divide any remaining addresses into other memory types grouped in the same way. In the 6800 and 6502 there are certain hardware restrictions that determine memory assignment. The most important of these is that the two microprocessors and the microcomputers built around them utilize page zero as the portion of memory to be set aside for special addressing modes. In both the 6800 and 6502, instructions referencing page zero are shorter as only one byte of address is required. In the case of the 6502, page zero type instructions are not only shorter but use page zero locations as indirect references to other locations in memory. Page zero in the 6800 and 6502 (locations 0 through FF_{16}) will therefore usually be used for RAM storage except in special hardware. Since it is usually easier to work with contiguous blocks of memory, RAM storage in the 6800 and 6502 microcomputers will probably occupy locations 0 on up to the limit of RAM. In addition, the 6502 requires RAM storage for the memory stack, and that memory stack must be in locations 100_{16} through $1FF_{16}$.

The second hardware limitation for all three microprocessors is that of interrupt address assignment. In the 8080 case, addresses 0, 10, 20, 30, 40, 50, 60, and 70_8 are used as interrupt vectors for eight *vectored* interrupts. These locations must hold instructions related to interrupt processing if interrupts are to be used in the microcomputer. Since these instructions are usually loaded with a program, this memory area should be RAM. In the 6800 and 6502 cases, the interrupts are handled by reserving locations $FFF8$-$FFFF_{16}$ or $FFFA$-$FFFF_{16}$ as interrupt vectors that point to the interrupt handling routines for the several types of interrupts that can occur. In microcomputers built around the 6800 and 6502, these locations are usually ROM or PROM along with other locations in the same memory area that contain a dedicated monitor program. In general, then, the highest memory addresses in the 6800 and 6502 microcomputers are dedicated

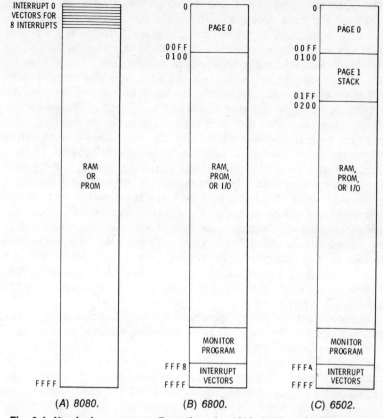

Fig. 8-1. Nominal memory configurations for 8080, 6800, and 6502 systems.

ROM memory. Fig. 8-1 illustrates the nominal memory configuration for the three types of microprocessors.

In each of the microcomputers based on the 8080, 6800, and 6502 a certain portion of the RAM area must be dedicated to the memory stack. In the 6502 case, the stack area is predefined as locations 100_{16} through $1FF_{16}$, providing 256_{10} bytes of stack area. In the 8080 and 6800 case, the stack area may be anywhere in the RAM area of memory, and is not limited as far as size. In all cases the stack area is a *LIFO* stack, or Last-In First-Out stack. This type of stack can be compared to a dinner-plate stacker found in restaurants which is periodically filled with dinner plates by busboys as customers take the top plate for their meal. The first plate taken off was the last one put in.

The stack area is accessible to the programmer and is utilized in a number of different ways. Firstly, the programmer may *push* a byte of data into the stack or as many bytes of data as he wishes. Conversely, he may *pull* or *pop* the last byte of data or several bytes of data from the stack. There are instructions to either push one byte or pull or pop one byte at a time from the stack. Used in this way, the stack is a temporary storage area. The second way the stack area may be used is in *CALLing subroutines* in the program. The CALL instruction or jump to subroutine or branch to subroutine transfers control as in an ordinary jump, but at the same time stores the program counter in the stack. Another instruction at the end of the subroutine returns from the subroutine and pops the program counter contents that were pushed into the stack initially. The stack actions taken during subroutine usage permit subroutine *reentrancy* (discussed in later chapters) and generally make things easier for the programmer in temporarily saving the contents of registers while he uses the registers in the subroutine. The third way the stack is utilized is by interrupt processing. As an interrupt occurs, the current location of the program counter, the state of the flags in the cpu, and certain other cpu registers are pushed into the stack. This is known as *saving the environment* and permits an easy return to the interrupted area of the program after the interrupt has been processed. The return is made by a special return-from-interrupt instruction which pops the data off in the same order as it was pushed into the stack.

The stack pointer always points to the next location in the stack area to be used by a push, CALL, or incoming interrupt. It is adjusted as each byte of data is pushed into the stack to point to the next location. It is adjusted the opposite direction when data is pulled from the stack. It is always the programmer's responsibility to initialize the stack pointer to point to the "top of stack" and to make certain that the same amount of data is pulled from the stack as is pushed into the stack. Were this not the case, the kitchen could conceivably be inundated with dinner plates in a manner reminiscent of *The Sorcerer's Apprentice*. Or, in memory, this could result in stack area overflow with the stack overflowing into the program area as more data was put into the stack than was taken out. Specific examples of how the stack is used are discussed in the following chapters. Chapter 9 covers stack operation for programmable pushes and pulls and subroutine use while Chapter 11 covers interrupt stack actions.

Microcomputer
Instruction Sets

This chapter covers a subject touched upon in earlier chapters, the instruction repertoire of each of the three microprocessors covered in the book. The instruction repertoire of the microprocessor is the same as the instruction repertoire of the microcomputer built around it since the instruction set is built into the LSI chip. Differences between microcomputers based upon the same microprocessor would never be in instruction implementation, but in the memory configuration, I/O addresses, bus arrangement, and instruction *mnemonics* used for the assembler, to mention some obvious areas where microcomputers would differ.

Just as in the addressing modes, instructions for the three microprocessors at first appear different, but fall into one of several groups. Although different sets of instruction groups could be argued, the groups defined here are the following:

1. Instructions that move data
2. Arithmetic and logical instructions
3. Shifts
4. Jumps and branches and jumps and branches to subroutines
5. Register and memory increments and decrements
6. Compare and test
7. Stack pulls and pops
8. Flag-type instructions
9. Special instructions

Since the instructions *are* different between microprocessors, each of the groups is discussed in general and then specifically for each of the three microprocessors, so that the reader may skip over the micro-processors with which he is not concerned. A complete set of instructions based upon the above nine categories is included for each of the three microprocessors in the appendixes.

GROUP 1 INSTRUCTIONS

Group number 1, instructions that move data, include instructions that move one byte of data between memory and a cpu register, instructions that move one byte of data from one cpu register to another cpu register, instructions that move two bytes of data between cpu registers, and immediate type instructions that load cpu registers or memory with immediate values in the instruction itself.

The 8080 Group 1 Instructions

The A accumulator can be loaded from memory by an LDA, LDAX B, or LDAX D instruction. The first is a direct type of addressing, while the other two are indexed types using register pairs B,C or D,E. LHLD loads register pair H,L directly from memory location m (into register L) and memory location m+1 (into register H). LXI B, LXI D, LXI H, and LXI SP load a two-byte immediate value in the instruction into the specified register pair. MVI M and MVI R move one byte of immediate data into the specified memory location M or cpu register R, using register pair H,L as an index register. MOV M,R, MOV R,M, and MOV R1,R2 move one byte of data from R to M, from M to R, or from register R2 to R1, respectively. The first two use register pair H,L as an index register. SHLD stores H,L, directly into memory locations m (L) and m+1 (H). SPHL transfers the contents of H,L to the stack pointer register SP. STA, STAX B, and STAX D store the contents of the A register into memory. STAX B and STAX D use register pairs B,C and D,E as index registers. The XCHG swaps the contents of D,E and H,L, while XTHL swaps H,L with the current memory locations that are the *top of stack*. Location m from the stack is swapped with L and location m+1 from the stack is swapped with H for XTHL.

The 6800 Group 1 Instructions

CLR zeroes a memory location, while CLRA and CLRB clear the A or B register, respectively. CLR may be indexed or extended addressing. The accumulators are loaded or stored by LDAA and LDAB or STAA and STAB, all of which are direct, indexed, or extended addressing types. TAB and TBA transfer the contents of the A accumulator to B or vice versa. The index register or stack pointer register can be loaded or stored by LDX, LDS or STX, STS, all of which are direct, indexed, or extended addressing types. The index register may be transferred to the stack pointer by the TXS instruction, while TSX does the opposite. The condition codes, treated as a register, may be transferred to the A accumulator by TPA.

The 6502 Group 1 Instructions

The accumulator, X register, or Y register may be loaded or stored from or to memory by LDA, LDX, LDY, STA, STX, and STY, respectively. LDA, LDX, and LDY may be immediate. The accumulator, X register, Y register, and stack pointer may be transferred to another cpu register by the following instructions, where the second letter represents the source register and the third letter represents the destination: TAX, TAY, TSX, TXA, TXS, TYA.

GROUP 2 INSTRUCTIONS

Group 2 instructions, arithmetic and logical, are generally instructions working with two operands and performing adds, subtracts, ANDs, ORs, exclusive ORs, and adds and subtracts with carries. The condition codes and flags are usually set on the result of the operation.

The 8080 Group 2 Instructions

ACI and ADI add the one-byte immediate operand to the contents of the A register either with the current state of the carry (ACI) or without (ADI). Likewise, ADC M and ADD M add a memory operand to the A register with or without carry, and ADC R and ADD R add the specified other cpu register to the A register with or without carry. The memory reference instructions use H,L as an index register. ANA M, ANA R, and ANI perform ANDs on the A register with a memory operand, cpu register, or immediate value, respectively. DAA performs the decimal adjust previously explained on the A register. The contents of register pair B,C, D,E, H,L, or the stack pointer can be added to the contents of the H,L registers by instructions DAD B, DAD D, DAD H, or DAD SP, respectively. ORA M, ORA R, and ORI perform logical ORs on the contents of the A register and a memory operand, cpu register, or immediate value. The SBB M, SBB R, SBI, SUB M, SUB R, and SUI instructions perform subtracts with or without borrow in the same fashion as the corresponding add instructions. XRA M, XRA R, and XRI perform exclusive ORs on the contents of the A register and a memory, cpu register, or immediate operand.

The 6800 Group 2 Instructions

An add and subtract of a memory operand or immediate operand with or without carry can be done by ADDA, ADDB, ADCA, ADCB, SUBA, SUBB, SBCA, or SBCB. Direct, indexed, or extended addressing modes may be used for the memory operand. The last letter of the mnemonic stands for the accumulator used. Similarly, an AND, exclusive OR, or OR may be performed by ANDA, ANDB, EORA, EORB, ORAA, or ORAB. In addition, the A and B accumulators may be added with the result going to the A accumulator by the ABA instruction. The SBA performs a subtract in the same manner. A ones's complement or two's complement can be performed on the contents of A, B, or a memory location by COMA, COMB, COM, NEGA, NEGB, or NEG. Lastly, the decimal adjust operation can be performed by DAA.

The 6502 Group 2 Instructions

An add or subtract with carry on the contents of the accumulator and a memory location or immediate operand may be performed by ADC or SBC. No add or subtract *without* carry is possible, necessitating clearly the carry before many adds and setting the carry before many subtracts. An AND, exclusive OR, and OR can be done with a memory or immediate operand and the accumulator by AND, EOR, and ORA.

GROUP 3 INSTRUCTIONS

Group 3 instructions are the shift instructions. There are three types of shifts: rotates, arithmetic shifts, and logical shifts. Rotates move the contents of a register or memory location one bit right or left with the data rotating back into the opposite side of the location. In some cases the data is rotated through the carry flag. Logical shifts move the data one bit right or left with a zero filling the vacated bit position. The carry flag is usually set by the bit shifted out. Arithmetic shifts *sign extend* the sign bit position so that on a right or left shift the same sign of the operand is preserved.

The 8080 Group 3 Instructions

All shift instructions in the 8080 are rotates. RAR rotates the A register right through the carry, RAL rotates A left through the carry, and RLC and RRC simply rotate the A register left or right. The first two shifts are essentially nine-bit shifts, with the "old" state of the carry shifting into the vacated bit position, and the bit shifted out of the register setting the carry. The last two shifts are 8-bit shifts with the bit shifting out of the register rotating around to the other end, and also affecting the carry.

The 6800 Group 3 Instructions

The A register, B register, or a memory location can be shifted in rotation arithmetically, or logically right by ROLA, ROLB, ROL,

RORA, RORB, ROR, ASLA, ASLB, ASL, ASRA, ASRB, ASR, LSRA, LSRB, or LSR. When a rotate is used, the shift is actually nine bits as the carry is used. The "old" state of the carry replaces the vacated bit position, while the bit shifted out sets the "new" state of the carry. The arithmetic left shifts set the carry of the state of the sign bit and a zero fills the least significant bit position. The sign bit is not preserved in this case. The logical shifts fill the sign bit position with a zero, and the least significant bit is shifted into the carry.

The 6502 Group 3 Instructions

The accumulator or a memory location can be shifted in rotation, arithmetically left, or logically right by ROL, ROR, ASL, or LSR. The ROL and ROR instructions rotate through the carry. The arithmetic shift sets the carry to the state of the sign bit and a zero fills the least significant bit position. The logical shift fills the sign bit position with a zero and the least significant bit is shifted into the carry.

GROUP 4 INSTRUCTIONS

Group 4 instructions include unconditional jumps or branches, conditional jumps based upon the current settings of cpu flags, subroutine calls (conditional and unconditional), and returns from subroutines.

The 8080 Group 4 Instructions

The JMP instruction unconditionally jumps to the specified memory address without affecting the stack. Conditional jumps can be made on the state of the carry, minus, zero, and parity flags. JC, JM, JNC, JNZ, JP, JPE, JPO, and JZ are jumps on carry, minus, no carry, no zero, positive, parity even, parity odd, and zero, respectively. The stack is not affected. CALLs to subroutines may be made conditionally or unconditionally. When a call is acted upon the current contents of the program counter are put into the stack, and the stack pointer register is decremented by two for the two bytes of the PC. The unconditional CALL is CALL while conditional CALLS can be made for the same conditions as the jumps—CC, CM, CNC, CNZ, CP, CPE, CPO, and CZ. At the end of the subroutine a return is effected by a RET type instruction, conditional or unconditional. When the return is made, the first two bytes at top of stack are put into the PC, causing transfer of control to the address after the CALL. The stack pointer is incremented by two. The unconditional return is RET, while conditional returns are made by RC, RM, RNC, RNZ, RP, RPE, RPO, and RZ. The last instruction in this group is the PCHL instruction which transfers the contents of the H,L registers to the program counter, essentially an unconditional jump.

The 6800 Group 4 Instructions

Unconditional branches in the 6800 include the BRA or Branch Always instruction, which is a relative addressing type only and the JMP instruction, which is indexed or extended. Conditional branches not affecting the stack are made on carry clear, carry set, zero, greater or equal to zero, greater than zero, higher, less than or equal to zero, lower or same, less than zero, minus, not zero, overflow clear, overflow set, or plus—BCC, BCS, BEQ, BGE, BGT, BHI, BLE, BLS, BLT, BMI, BNE, BVC, BVS, and BPL. All of these are relative type addressing only. Branch to Subroutine, BSR, and Jump to Subroutine, JSR, are identical in their actions except that the former is relative addressing while the latter is indexed or extended. The contents of the program counter are pushed into the stack and the stack pointer is decremented by two. A transfer to the subroutine location is then made. RTS, Return From Subroutine, reverses the procedure, restoring the contents of the program counter and incrementing the stack pointer by two.

The 6502 Group 4 Instructions

The 6502 instruction JMP causes an unconditional jump. It can be absolute or indirect. Relative type conditional branches can be made by BCC, BCS, BEQ, BMI, BNE, BPL, BVC, and BVS, which branch on carry equals zero, carry equals one, equal, minus, not zero, plus, no overflow, and overflow. None of the above affect the stack. JSR jumps to subroutine while RTS returns from the subroutine. In the former, the contents of the program counter are pushed into the stack and the stack pointer decremented by two; in the latter the PC is loaded from the stack and the stack pointer incremented by two.

GROUP 5 INSTRUCTIONS

Group 5 instructions are, in general, instructions that increment or decrement registers by one count. This operation is common while using index registers to count the number of passes through a loop or to access contiguous memory locations.

The 8080 Group 5 Instructions

Incrementing a memory location or cpu register by one or decrementing a memory location or cpu register by one is performed by INR M, INR R, DCR M, and DCR R. These are increments and decrements of one register or memory location only. The H,L register is used as an index register in the memory location case. INX B, INX D, INX H, INX SP, DCX B, DCX D, DCX H, and DCX SP increment or decrement register pairs B,C, D,E, H,L, or the stack pointer. These are increments and decrements of 16 bits at a time.

The 6800 Group 5 Instructions

The A accumulator, B accumulator, or a memory location can be incremented or decremented by instructions INCA, INCB, INC, DECA, DECB, and DEC. INC and DEC can be indexed or extended. The index register or stack pointer can also be decremented or incremented by DEX, DES, INX, and INSE.

The 6502 Group 5 Instructions

Index registers X and Y or a memory location can be incremented or decremented by INX, INY, INC, DEX, DEY, or DEC. The memory location case can be one of several addressing modes.

GROUP 6 INSTRUCTIONS

Group 6 type instructions compare two operands and set the cpu flags on the result of the comparison, or test one operand only.

The 8080 Group 6 Instructions

A memory operand, register operand, or immediate operand can be compared with the contents of the A register by CMP M, CMP R, or CPI. The H,L registers are used as index register or pointer in the case of the memory reference instruction.

The 6800 Group 6 Instructions

A memory operand of 8 bits can be compared to the contents of the A or B accumulator by CMPA or CMPB, which may be any memory reference addressing mode. The two accumulators may be compared by CBA. The index register may be compared with a two-byte memory operand by the CPX instruction, which may be any memory reference addressing mode. The Bit Test instruction, BITA or BITB, performs a logical AND on the contents of the specified accumulator and memory operand and sets the condition codes accordingly. Neither operand is changed. TST, TSTA, and TSTB test a memory operand, the A accumulator, or B accumulator for zero or minus and set the appropriate flags.

The 6502 Group 6 Instructions

A memory operand can be compared to the contents of the accumulator, X register, or Y register by CMP, CPX, or CPY. The

BIT instruction performs a logical AND on the contents of the accumulator and a memory operand and sets the condition codes accordingly. Neither operand is changed.

GROUP 7 INSTRUCTIONS

Group 7 instructions are used to push or pop from the stack. Either 8-bit or 16-bit operands may be used. The stack pointer is adjusted by the appropriate amount as the transfers are made, decrementing the stack by one for each byte pushed and incrementing by one for each byte popped or pulled.

The 8080 Group 7 Instructions

The A register and flags, designated PSW, register pairs B,C, D,E, or H,L can be pushed or popped from the stack by PUSH PSW, PUSH B, PUSH D, PUSH H, POP PSW, POP B, POP D, and POP H.

The 6800 Group 7 Instructions

The contents of either the A or B accumulator can be pushed or pulled from the stack by PSHA, PSHB, PULA, or PULB.

The 6502 Group 7 Instructions

The accumulator can be pushed into or pulled from the stack by PHA or PLA. The processor status (flags) may be pushed into or pulled from the stack by PHP or PLP.

GROUP 8 INSTRUCTIONS

Group 8 instructions are instructions that set or reset flags in the cpu, either prior to performing an arithmetic operation dependent upon the flag, or to set some condition such as enabling interrupts in the cpu.

The 8080 Group 8 Instructions

Interrupts are disabled or enabled in the 8080 by the DI and EI instructions, which reset or set the I flag in the cpu. The only other flag that can be set or reset is the carry, which is set by an STC instruction and complemented by a CMC instruction.

The 6800 Group 8 Instructions

The carry flag in the 6800 can be set or reset by an SEC or CLC instruction. The interrupt mask can be enabled or disabled by an SEI or CLI instruction. Overflow can be set or cleared by an SEV or CLV instruction. All of the condition codes in the "condition code register" can be set to the desired configuration by the TAP instruction, which transfers the contents of the accumulator to the condition codes.

The 6502 Group 8 Instructions

The C,D (decimal mode), and I flags in the 6502 can be cleared or set by instructions CLC, CLD, CLI, SEC, SED, and SEI. The overflow flag can be cleared by CLV.

GROUP 9 INSTRUCTIONS

The remaining instructions fall into none of the above groups. They are generally instructions which are unique to the microprocessor. All three microprocessors, however, share the common instruction NOP, a "do nothing" or no operation instruction.

The 8080 Group 9 Instructions

The two instructions OUT and IN perform transfers of data from the A register to an output device or from the output device to the A register as previously discussed. RST, or Restart, is a special instruction used to facilitate the processing of interrupts. It is discussed in Chapter 11.

The 6800 Group 9 Instructions

The 6800 has three special instructions related to interrupt processing: RTI, Return from Interrupt, SWI, Software Interrupt, and WAI, Wait for Interrupt. They are discussed in Chapter 11.

The 6502 Group 9 Instructions

The 6502 has two special instructions related to interrupt processing: BRK, Break, and RTI, Return from Interrupt. They are discussed in Chapter 11.

Microcomputer
Input/Output

There are two methods for external I/O devices to communicate with the microcomputer. The first of these is I/O via the cpu accumulator and an I/O instruction, usually called *programmed I/O*. The second is by communication directly with the memory in the microcomputer, bypassing cpu registers completely. I/O via I/O instructions is the most common and is used for low-speed I/O devices, while direct memory access is used for high-speed I/O devices such as floppy discs.

To perform an output to an I/O device in the 8080 by the first method, an OUT instruction is executed, after first loading the A register with the data to be transferred. The data is transferred to the data bus, and the I/O address in the OUT instruction is transferred to the eight least significant lines of the address bus. Two control signals are brought up to inform the I/O device controller that an output is being performed. The I/O device controller recognizes its I/O device address and the control signals and transfers the 8 bits of data to its internal buffer. In the 6800 and 6502, the process is similar except that there are no actual I/O instructions. An output is performed by loading the cpu accumulator(s) with the data to be transferred and then performing a STA. The data in the accumulator is transferred to the data bus, the address in the STA is transferred to the address bus, and the device controller recognizes its address. The device address is unique and cannot be used as a memory address as previously discussed. The 8 bits of data are then transferred to the internal buffer just as in the 8080 case. An input operation is similar. The device controller recognizes its address, detects that this is an input operation (or memory read in the 6800 and 6502 case), and transfers an 8-bit data byte from its internal buffer to the data bus. An IN instruction is used in the 8080 case, while a LDA is used in the 6800 and 6502.

The total execution time of the input or output is on the order of 5 microseconds. Each time that the IN, OUT, LDA, or STA instruction is executed another byte of data is transferred. To transfer 64 bytes of data, as, for example, to output a line of 64 characters to a video display, 64 discrete OUTs or STAs must be done. Each I/O device controller *buffers* the data. In the simplest case the device controller buffer consists of a one-byte register. In other cases, the buffer may be larger. The buffering is necessary to match the I/O device speed to the cpu speed. I/O device speeds vary over a wide range. A Teletype is able to transfer data at only 10 characters (or 10 bytes) per second. Audio cassettes operate from 30 bytes per second to 500 bytes per second. Video displays may transfer data at rates of 9600 bytes per second and above. Because all of these speeds are far lower than the cpu speeds in executing the I/O instructions, data is transmitted to the device controller's buffer in 5 microseconds or so, and the cpu is then free to continue with the next instruction.

There are several alternatives to timing the transfer of data to the I/O device. The first would be to time the interval between transfers of a byte so that the I/O device would have been assured of completing the last transfer. This is rather difficult since most I/O devices are not that synchronous. It is impossible to do when the device is completely asynchronous, as, for example, an operator hitting Teletype keys. A second alternative would be for the device controller to set a flag indicating that the I/O device was "ready." For a device that is transferring data into the microcomputer, the ready flag would mean that the next byte of data was available in the device controller's buffer. For a device that was accepting data, the ready flag would mean that the device had finished with the transfer of the last data byte and was ready to input the next into its buffer. This is the general scheme used in most microcomputer I/O today. A third alternative, having the device controller *interrupt* the cpu when a ready condition came up, is discussed in the next chapter.

Using the ready flag method of I/O means that the flag must somehow be tested. This means that another I/O operation must be done to read in the current state of the ready flag. The general approach to this is to assign another I/O device address to the status of the device, so that the device controller will recognize the request for device status and will send the status, rather than a data byte. Obviously, in a more complicated I/O device, more status bits could be employed. For example, IBM-compatible tape transports would have status bits indicating a parity error on the last read or write, tape at load point, tape at end-of-tape, and so forth. Conversely, in some cases it may be necessary to send *control* bits out to the device controller in addition to data. An example of this would be control information to an audio cassette interface which would start or stop the cassette motor. In the general case, then, device controllers would be able to supply information on the status of the device, accept control data to control the device, and buffer data for transmission to the device.

The maximum data transfer rate to a device under the method described above is determined by how long it takes to transfer each byte of data. Assuming that a block of data to be transferred is nicely set up in memory in a contiguous block, and that only the ready flag has to be tested before the next byte is transferred, the I/O procedure would go something like this:

1. At end of block? If not, go to 2; if so, done.
2. Get next byte of data from block.
3. Test ready. If not ready, go to 3; if ready, go to 4.
4. Execute I/O instruction.
5. Increment block pointer to next byte.
6. Go to 1.

If the average instruction time for the above loop was 5 microseconds and there were 8 instructions executed for each byte, it would take 40 microseconds to transfer one byte of data to the device. This corresponds to a data transfer rate of 25,000 bytes per second. In addition to the transfer rate limitation, the cpu must continually execute the I/O loop; it is not free to do any other processing. It is completely *I/O bound*. For these reasons, DMA is used to interface to high-speed devices such as some floppy discs and certain graphics displays. In some cases the speeds of these devices exceed the maximum transfer rates of the first method, and the cpu is free to do other processing while DMA occurs on a cycle-stealing basis.

The device controller that does the DMA operates in the following fashion. Using special control codes, a starting memory address is sent to the controller, along with the number of bytes to be transferred. These are both sent via the execution of I/O instructions. Another control code is given to start the DMA transfer. The program now can go on to any other processing that is required. Periodically it may test a flag from the device controller to see if DMA has completed, or an interrupt may occur at DMA completion.

While the program is doing other processing, the device controller is performing DMAs at a rate consistent with the I/O device. If, for example, the I/O device operates at 100,000 bytes per second, a new byte of data must be transferred every 10 microseconds. Every 10 microseconds the device controller would bring up a control line to the microprocessor that would cause the microprocessor to suspend execution. The cpu would stop at a certain point in execution of the current instruction and send an acknowledge signal telling the device controller that execution had stopped. The device controller would then be free to send a memory address over the system address bus and pick up the next byte of data from system memory which would then be transferred to the I/O device. The control line would then be brought down to enable the cpu to continue with the current instruction. This type of direct memory access is completely invisible to the program. Every 10 microseconds a new byte is read from memory while the cpu momentarily suspends operation. With a memory operating at 500-nanosecond rates typically, this means that every 10 microseconds 0.5 microsecond is devoted to DMAs, or that the cpu is slowed down by 5 percent.

Given the two methods of I/O, how are various I/O devices interfaced to the microcomputer? One of the more common types of interfaces offered as plug-in options to microcomputers is the serial I/O option, sometimes called an *asynchronous I/O option* or *asynchronous serial I/O option*. This option interfaces to I/O devices that handle data in serial fashion such as all Teletype equipment, old or new, and equipment designed to replace Teletype equipment, such as commercial alphanumeric displays. Equipment such as this handles data in serial bit streams, as historically data could more easily be transmitted over telephone-type lines in serial fashion. The serial interface must receive a byte for output and then send it over to the serial device a bit at a time in a prearranged format. For Baudot-type Teletypes the format is a zero bit, followed by five data bits, least significant bit first, followed by a one bit. The first six bits are spaced 22 milliseconds apart, while the last bit is 31 milliseconds, making a total transmission time per character of 163 milliseconds. For newer model Teletype equipment the format is a zero bit, followed by seven data bits, least significant bit first, followed by a parity bit, followed by two one bits. Each bit is spaced 9.09 milliseconds apart, making the total transmission time 100 milliseconds per character or a maximum rate of 110 bits per second, or 110 *baud*. Teletype replacement equipment and other asynchronous equipment operate at standard rates of 110, 300, 600, 1200, 2400, 4800, and 9600 baud, and many serial interfaces will handle these rates with simple hardware strapping on the module. In addition full-duplex or half-duplex operation will probably be offered. Full-duplex operation means that a character can be transmitted either direction simultaneously, while half-duplex permits transmission in one direction at a time only. Teletypes and communications equipment can operate in either mode. Another option the serial interface may offer is a choice of signal level. The standard Teletype is called 20-millampere current loop while communications-oriented equipment uses a standard voltage and signal type known as RS-232. Lastly, more than one *port* may be offered on the serial option to enable communication with more than one serial device.

The second type of general-purpose I/O interface is a parallel-interface option. The parallel-interface option may offer several input ports and several output ports. Each port has its own address and buffer latch. By addressing a port data can be read from or output to the latches. With some minimal additional interfacing, standard computer peripherals that are oriented toward transfers of one byte of parallel data can be used on the microcomputer. These devices are such things as high-speed punched–paper-tape readers, high-speed paper-tape punches, character printers, line printers, and the like.

While the devices discussed above are primarily "off-the-shelf" pieces of equipment that can be interfaced to the microcomputer by a general-purpose interface, there is a second category of I/O equipment that has been developed for microcomputers, generally for the 8080, 6800, and 6502 based micros. Equipment in this category ranges from video boards that provide alphanumeric or graphics displays and audio cassette equipment to complete floppy disc systems. The complexity of the interface will vary with the peripheral device. Some interfaces will use only programmed I/O. A typical example of this type would be an audio cassette interface which provides control outputs and status inputs and transfers data a byte at a time via the cpu accumulator. Interrupt capability may or may not be offered with the interface. Other interfaces will utilize both programmed I/O and DMA transfers, such as some floppy disc systems or the popular Dazzler color display. In general the package will be complete, that is, the peripheral device will have a complete interface ready to plug into the existing microcomputer bus, or at least ready after some kit building. In addition most equipment offers fairly good documentation, including pertinent applications software to drive the I/O device.

A third category of I/O interfaces are the special purpose interfaces for experimenters. These include analog-to-digital and digital-to-analog interfaces, skeleton or prototyping boards, PROM programming boards, EPROM boards, relay driver or discrete output and input boards, and the like. Using these boards, the hobbyist is relieved of some of the research and development effort in designing his own unique interfaces to fulfill his microcomputer system requirements.

Microcomputer
Interrupt Processing

One day the author chanced to see a novice programmer attempt to ask an acerbic old-timer a question regarding some microcomputer code. The old-timer snapped, "Don't interrupt me, I'm busy!" The novice walked away, muttering that the old-timer was "like a computer, not a human being." The novice, gentle reader, was decidedly wrong. Computers like to be interrupted, unlike some programmers.

The basic idea about microcomputer interrupts is that microcomputers are usually much faster than I/O devices, and in some cases it is convenient to have an external stimulus or interrupt notify the microcomputer that an I/O operation is done or that an I/O operation can be started. Take the example of Teletype I/O, which proceeds at 10 characters per second. It only takes perhaps 20 microseconds to get a byte of data, test Teletype status, and output the data byte to the Teletype, It then takes the logic in the Teletype controller 100,000 microseconds to send the byte out to the Teletype in serial form. In that 100,000 microseconds 20,000 instructions could be executed. Why not use that time to process other data? This is indeed possible under interrupt control.

A second example of interrupt usage is that of a high-priority interrupt that occurs infrequently, but when it does it signifies a condition that requires immediate attention. If your microcomputer system is connected to a burglar alarm system, for example, an interrupt might occur when one of the window switches is tripped, and the microcomputer could then take the appropriate action. Another example of this in the 6800 and 6502 is an internal interrupt called NMI or "nonmaskable interrupt," which in some cases is used to signify a powerdown condition. If this interrupt occurs, the microprocessor is about to lose power and appropriate action can be taken.

Both of the examples above, the Teletype I/O and the burglar alarm, could easily be programmed without the use of interrupts. In many manufacturers' programs, output and input to a Teletype occurs in a "wait" loop in which the microcomputer waits for Teletype ready status and then transfers the next character. The burglar alarm could be handled by *polling* or periodically testing the burglar alarm input for a zero input condition that signals a tripped switch. However, as microcomputer software gets more sophisticated and memories become less expensive, *interrupt-driven* software will be used more frequently. In addition, since the interrupt structure already exists in the microprocessor and many I/O controllers, interrupts are an inexpensive way to increase the *throughput,* or effective speed, of a microcomputer system.

Let's illustrate how the throughput of a typical microcomputer system could be increased and what actions occur during interrupt processing. A good example for this would be the processing involved in a game of "Life." Life is a popular microcomputer game that is explained in detail in back issues of *Scientific American.* It involves representing successive generations of points on a matrix of squares similar to a checkerboard. Each point lives or dies dependent upon the number of neighbors it has in the preceding generation. In addition points can be born where none existed previously. The net effect is a constantly changing pattern of points that emulates civilization, with colonies of points dying over many generations, other colonies reproducing themselves indefinitely (or so it first appears), and wild groups of Young Turks suddenly appearing and just as quickly disappearing. Since each generation is dependent upon the preceding generation, each point must be compared to the preceding number of neighbors, necessitating a lot of processing from one generation to the next. A typical amount of processing to calculate the next generation for a 64-by-32 matrix might be on the order of five seconds.

If we assume in our example that a video display at 120 characters per second is being used, it would take about 8½ seconds to output each generation on the screen. If interrupts were not used, the total time for processing and output would be about 13½ seconds. With interrupts, the total time for each generation would be very nearly 8½ seconds, or the I/O time only. Once a new generation was processed and put in a buffer ready for output, processing for the next generation could be started in a second buffer. This processing would be interrupted every time the last character output to the screen was done, or every 8 milliseconds. When the interrupt occurred, the *interrupt routine* would pick up the next character to be output to the screen, transmit it to the video display controller, set up the display controller to provide an interrupt after the 8 milliseconds it takes before the controller is again ready, and then return to the interrupted point in the processing program to continue processing of the next generation. The net result of this would be that the processing portion of the program would be interrupted every 8 milliseconds or so to do possibly 80 microseconds of computation to output the next character, adding about 1 percent to processing time, and less than 1 percent to the time required to perform I/O.

When the interrupt signifying that the video display is ready for the next character appears, the processing program may be executing any instruction. At the end of the current instruction the cpu recognizes the interrupt, transfers control of the program to a special interrupt processing routine, after first pushing the contents of the program counter into the stack. Pushing the PC into the stack enables the interrupt processing program to return to the point at which it was interrupted, after interrupt processing has been completed. Since the interrupt could have occurred at any instruction, the current states of the cpu flags must also be pushed into the stack. If the instruction following the interrupted point was a conditional jump on zero, for example, and somewhere in the interrupt routine the zero flag was altered, a return to the interrupted point *must* restore the state of the zero flag. In addition, if the interrupt routine uses any cpu registers they must also be saved in the stack before use. The return to the interrupted instruction must be made with the cpu flags and all cpu registers exactly the same as they were before the interrupt. *Saving the environment* is facilitated by use of the stack instructions to push the environment upon entering the interrupt routine and to pull or pop the environment upon leaving the interrupt routine.

In this manner interrupts can be used to speed up overall processing. The interrupted program will never be aware of the infrequent interrupts and processing can be overlapped with I/O servicing. The above example illustrated a single-level interrupt. Only one type of interrupt could occur. The 8080 permits up to eight unique interrupts, the 6800 allows four unique interrupts, and the 6502 allows three interrupts. Special problems of *reentrancy* in software are discussed in later chapters. Interrupt hardware implementation in the 8080, 6800, and 6502 is discussed below.

The 8080 microprocessor chip has three signals associated with interrupts, INT, INTE, and INTA. An interrupt will be recognized by the cpu if the interrupt flag in the cpu is set. If the interrupt flag is not set, the interrupt from the external I/O controller will be forgotten if it occurs momentarily. In some cases the external device will supply a constant signal level for the interrupt until the interrupt is *recognized,* and in this case the interrupt will remain until the flag is set. In most cases the interrupt will remain until it is recognized, but this is a function of the device controller and the specific microcomputer. The interrupt is input to the microprocessor over the INT line. If the interrupt occurs and the cpu interrupt flag has been enabled by an EI instruction, the cpu recognizes the interrupt condition after the current instruction has been executed, but before the next instruction can be executed. The cpu then sends a special status signal, designated INTA, out to the interrupting device controller. INTA, or interrupt acknowledge, informs the external device controller that the cpu has recognized the interrupt. At a certain interval after the INTA the interrupting device then *"jams"* a restart (RST) instruction onto the cpu data bus. The cpu picks up the restart instruction and executes it on the next instruction cycle just as it would execute any instruction.

The RST instruction in the 8080 is a unique instruction designed for interrupt processing. It is really a one-byte CALL. The length must be one byte only, because the cpu is capable of picking up only one byte in the interval after the INTA has been sent to the external device controller. Like any CALL, the current contents of the program counter are pushed into the stack. The program counter points to the instruction that was to be executed just before the interrupt occurred. Unlike the CALL, the program counter is not loaded with an address from bytes 2 and 3 of the instruction as they do not exist. The PC is loaded with eight times the 3-bit NNN field from the RST instruction. NNN may be 0 through 7, and loading the PC with $8 \times N$ would therefore load 0, 8, 16, 24, 32, 40, 48, or 56 into the program counter and cause a resultant transfer to these program locations. There are therefore eight *vectors* or pointers to locations that are possible with the 8080. Each vector points to a separate interrupt processing area where the normal saving of the environment occurs, or at least where a JMP is made to an interrupt processing area where the environment is saved. At the end of interrupt processing the environment is restored and an RET instruction is executed. The RET instruction restores the location of the interrupted instruction to the program counter and then processing resumes from the interrupted location.

Since there are eight vectors in the 8080, there may be up to 8 devices with unique interrupts. It is the responsibility of the interrupting device controller to request interrupt service when required by bringing up an interrupt line. Since other devices may also be requesting service, there is usually a separate *priority interrupt module* that recognizes all interrupt requests (as many as 8), determines which has the greater priority, brings up the INT line to the cpu, and jams the proper RST instruction onto the data bus when the INTA line goes out. This avoids ambiguities that would arise if each device controller could set the INT line independently. The latter approach, taken in many minicomputers, involves "daisy chaining" the interrupt lines from one device controller to the next to establish priorities, and is generally less straightforward than the priority interrupt module approach.

There are four types of interrupts in the 6800 microprocessor chip. One of these, RES, is a reset interrupt and is used in the power-on initialization. Implemented in a microcomputer, a power-on condition results in the program counter being loaded with the contents of memory locations FFFE and $FFFF_{16}$. This transfers control to a special power-on interrupt sequence. A second interrupt, NMI, is used for powerdown conditions in some applications. When this interrupt occurs, the following cpu data is pushed into the stack in the given order: PC_L, PC_H, INX_L, INX_H, ACCA, ACCB, condition codes. The program counter is then loaded with the contents of memory locations FFFC and $FFFD_{16}$, effecting transfer to the NMI, or nonmaskable interrupt sequence. Neither NMI or RES may be disabled by resetting the interrupt flag in the cpu condition codes. A third interrupt, SWI or software interrupt, is produced by execution of the SWI instruction with the interrupt flag in the cpu on. It causes the cpu registers and flags to be pushed into the stack in the order given above. The program counter is then loaded with the contents of locations $FFFA_{16}$ and $FFFB_{16}$, causing transfer of control to the SWI interrupt handling routine. The primary *external* interrupt in the 6800 is the IRQ interrupt. An external interrupt causes the same stack storage as previously discussed and causes the program counter to be loaded with the contents of memory locations $FFF8_{16}$ and $FFF9_{16}$. Since there is only one external interrupt (although NMI could be used as a second external interrupt in a pinch), some means must be provided to implement multiple I/O interrupts if more than one interrupt from an I/O device is required. Implementation of this is dependent upon the microcomputer, but generally involves ORing all external interrupts together. When the interrupt occurs, a poll is made of all possible interrupting devices. This involves reading the status from each device controller and testing an interrupt flag in the status to see whether an interrupt occurred from that particular device. If so, the program can then vector off into the specific interrupt handling routine for that device; the actual hardware interrupt however, IRQ, has already occurred at that point.

The 6502 microprocessor has three unique interrupts, RESET, NMI, and IRQ, and they are very similar to the 6800. RESET is used upon power-up and loads the contents of locations $FFFC_{16}$ and $FFFD_{16}$ into the program counter, transferring control to the restart routine. NMI pushes the PC and processor status register (flags) into the stack and then loads the program counter with the contents of locations $FFFA_{16}$ and $FFFB_{16}$, transferring control to the NMI interrupt routine. Both NMI and RESET are not disabled by the state of the interrupt flag in the cpu. IRQ is the external interrupt. It causes the same stack actions as NMI but loads the program counter with the contents of locations FFFE and $FFFF_{16}$, transferring control to the external interrupt routine. Since, as in the 6800, there is only one external interrupt, the same method of polling must be performed in software to determine which external devices have an active interrupt present. The RTI, return from interrupt instruction, pops the PC and processor status register from the stack, to partially restore the environment and return control to the interrupted location. Any cpu registers used in the interrupt routine, of course, must be initially saved in the stack and restored at the end of the interrupt processing.

Assembly Language Programming With Microcomputers

Assembly Language vs. Machine Language

Part 3 of this book will illustrate how to perform common operations on microcomputers, such as moving data, table operations, bit processing, and so on. In order to facilitate the understanding of the program examples, the programs will be written in *assembly language* format for the various microprocessors. In fact, many readers may be entering programs into their microcomputers in *machine language.* Machine language is nothing more than assembling the instructions of the program in octal or hexadecimal, whichever the manufacturer prefers for his microcomputer. To enter a 200-instruction program would mean writing down 200 8-bit values, expressed in binary, octal, or hexadecimal and keying them into the machine from the front panel, entering from the monitor program, or using a monitor program in conjunction with a hexadecimal keyboard to enter the values.

However, if machine language is to be used, it is still helpful to first write the program using assembly language *mnemonics* and *syntax* and then to hand assemble the mnemonics into assembly language values for entry. For this reason we will discuss the characteristics of the assembly languages used on the three machines.

A common assembly language line represents one instruction, and is of the form

      Label   *Operation Arguments*   *Comments*

An LDA (or LDAA) instruction, for example, might be represented by the assembly language line

      HERE   LDA   VALUE   GET CURRENT VALUE

The operation is the actual instruction mnemonic found in the manufacturer's literature. Many times this corresponds to the original mnemonic used by the microprocessor chip manufacturer. The arguments field of the assembly language line has the operands associated with the mnemonic. The LDA, for example, must have a memory address for the load, and memory location VALUE is that memory address in *symbolic form*. This will be explained shortly. The comments portion of the line is exactly that—comments describing what the current instruction accomplishes. The label field is an optional name of the location of the instruction, used in lieu of writing down the memory address of the instruction, since it may not immediately be known in a large program that is just being written.

The fact that it is difficult to keep track of the location of instructions while writing a program is the whole *raison d'etre* for symbolic assembly language form. If the reader was writing a 40-instruction program and a conditional jump had to be made near the start to the 38th instruction, he could indeed write

JNZ   213$_8$

if he knew for certain that the jump address was 213_8. If he had not written that portion of the program, however, it would be impossible to assign an address at the time of writing down the JNZ, and the operand field would have to be left blank, to be filled in later. In addition, suppose that the address were carefully calculated by assigning memory addresses to the instructions based on their one-, two-, or three-byte lengths and the absolute address was written down for the JNZ. If any instructions were added between the JNZ and the location to which the jump was to be made the address in the JNZ would have to be changed, along with other instructions that referenced locations beyond the added instructions. A final reason for using symbolic addresses instead of absolute addresses is that the program in symbolic form is not tied to a specific part of memory. It can be *reassembled* by hand or by assembler program to operate anywhere in memory.

Using symbolic addressing, locations are referenced by their name, and no absolute memory locations have to be written down for the arguments field of the instruction line. An example of this is the short program

```
START   LXI H,CLR-1   CLEAR AREA—1
        XRA A         ZERO A
LOOP    INX H         BUMP CLEAR POINTER
        MOV M,A       ZERO ONE LOCATION
        JMP LOOP      GO TO NEXT CLEAR
CLR     . . .
```

Although this is a short program to clear all of memory on an 8080, and should be located starting at location 0, all memory references were given symbolic names to illustrate that no absolute addresses had to be used. Once the program is written and checked over, it could be hand assembled. Start at the first instruction and write down the starting address. Then move to the second instruction and write down its address. If START was 000, then the next instruction is at 003, since the LXI is three bytes long. Now move through all the instructions, and assign a location for each instruction. The result will look somewhat like this:

```
000    START    LXI H,CLR-1    . . .
003             XRA  A         . . .
004    LOOP     INX  H         . . .
005             MOV  M,A        . . .
006             JMP LOOP        . . .
011    CLR      . . .
```

Now double-check the instruction lengths and addresses assigned. We are now ready to build a table of symbolic names. Although this is a short enough program to be able to inspect the names to find the absolute address, this is not always convenient in a large program. The table of names, or *symbol table,* has three entries: START, LOOP, and CLR. For convenience in long programs they are arranged in alphabetical order.

Name	Location
CLR	011
LOOP	004
START	000

The next step after the symbol table is to start at the beginning of the program and construct the instruction at each location. This is a two-step process. First the skeleton of the instruction is written down. This is the generic form of the instruction with no operands or special fields filled in. Then the operands are filled into the instruction. The operands will be immediate data values, register numbers, and memory locations. Whenever a symbolic reference is made the symbol table is consulted and the value of that symbol found and filled into the instruction. The result looks something like this:

Location	Data	Assembly Line Image		
000	041 010 000	START	LXI H,CLR-1	CLEAR AREA—1
003	257		XRA A	ZERO A
004	043	LOOP	INX H	BUMP CLEAR POINTER
005	167		MOV M,A	ZERO ONE LOCATION
006	303 004 000		JMP LOOP	GO TO NEXT CLEAR
011	. . .			

Congratulations! You have exactly duplicated what an assembler program does. The assembler has other niceties discussed below, but essentially goes through the same steps as described above. A typical assembler will consist of two *passes*. The first pass will calculate the length of each instruction and update a current location pointer. The symbol table is also constructed on the first pass, with all symbolic names and references entered in the table in alphabetical order. Each name is put into the table as encountered; therefore a symbol in an operand field is entered in the table if it has not been encountered as a name previously. In this case the symbol will be encountered somewhere beyond the current location. It is a *forward* reference. At the end of the first pass all symbols in the table should have been resolved with a value. If a symbol has not been resolved, it is an unsatisfied reference and an error. The assembler then reads in the source statement lines once again, and this time constructs the machine-language code, filling in the memory reference addresses and other fields with values from the operand field of the source line or with symbolic values from the symbol table. As each location is constructed, the location, data contents, and assembly line image is printed on the assembly listing device. A line number may also be printed in some assemblers. In addition, if there are errors connected with the line, *diagnostic* warnings are printed in the line. These are usually one-letter codes that specify the type of assembly error. At the same time that the current line is printed, or possibly during a third pass, the *object code* of the assembly is output in the form of punched paper tape, a magnetic tape file, a floppy disc file, or another usable form. The object code represents the machine language code of the program in a special *loader* format, which varies with the type of microcomputer. The object code can then be read into the microcomputer with another utility program, the loader program.

In addition to the normal instruction mnemonics for the defined microprocessor instructions, each assembler will have a set of *non-generative* operations that do not produce machine language code. These are called *pseudo-ops* for that reason. Each pseudo-op replaces the instruction mnemonic in the operation field of the assembly source line.

The ORG statement informs the assembler to set the location counter to a specified location. Instructions are then assembled from that point. For example,

ORG   2000

sets the assembler's location counter to 2000_8 (assuming that 2000 represents an octal location). ORGs can be used at any point in the program where required. Each time an ORG, or new *origin,* is used, the corresponding object code would contain some origin *load item* flag that would inform the loader of the new origin. The loader would then reset the load location counter and load the next data at the new origin.

An END pseudo-op is self-explanatory. An EQU, or equate pseudo-op, equates the name in the assembly line to the argument. The EQU statement

TTY   EQU   1

equates the name TTY to the value 1. The name TTY is placed in the symbol table when the pseudo-op is encountered (or before, if it is a forward reference) and the value of 1 is associated with TTY. Equates are useful for defining commonly used values. It is much easier to name the value 101101_2 CHK than to write out the value each time it is referred to in the program, for example.

The pseudo-op DS or similar names (Motorola uses RMB, Reserve Memory Bytes) defines storage in the program. By writing the pseudo-op and an argument, a certain number of unused data bytes are left unfilled by the assembler. The assembler location counter is incremented by the number of bytes specified in the argument field. At load time, the loader will usually not fill these locations, but will increment the loader location counter past the storage area. Note that the storage area should not follow executable code other than an unconditional jump. The storage area cannot be executed as instructions, of course. The start of each storage area can be named as required. A typical storage area for three variables computed in the program might look like this:

```
MANNY    DS  1    MAN HOURS FOR NEW YORK
MOE      DS  2    METHOD OF ENTRY
JACK     DS  2    JOB ACCESS KNOWLEDGE
```

Just as storage areas can be left unused for variables computed in the program, variables can be defined at assembly time for use during the program. These variables can also be named, and may consist of numeric variables, ASCII data, double-precision data values, and other data types, depending upon the assembler. The pseudo-op assembly line

PAGE   DW   'PAGE'

will produce the four ASCII bytes 120 101 107 105 in the data section of the listing, for example, with the assembler location counter correspondingly counting up the four locations. The assembly line

MASK1   DB   7

generates a data value of 7 at the current assembler location. This location is symbolically named MASK1 and an LDA MASK1 would load 7 into the accumulator.

The ORG, END, EQU, storage, and constant-definition pseudo-ops are the most commonly used pseudo-ops in microcomputers. Others that might be found are pseudo-ops related to naming the program tape or disc file manage, page and line formatting commands, and macro-related pseudo-ops that generate *macros* of more than one line of code. Another capability that is usually offered is *expression* use. An expression uses the operators $+$, $-$, $*$, $/$, and others, to create algebraic expressions. The location two bytes beyond location HERE could be referred to as HERE+2, for example. The length of a table starting at location DINNR and ending at DSERT could be computed by the *assembler* with proper use of the expression equated to STUFD:

```
DINNR    DB     'CHOWDER'
         DB     'TOSSED GREEN'
         DB     'AU GRATIN'
         DB     'PEAS AND ONIONS'
         DB     'STEAK'
         DB     'CHERRY PIE'
DSERT    DB     -1
STUFD    EQU    DSERT-DINNR
```

STUFD would be equated in the symbol table to the length in bytes of the DINNR table ASCII messages. In this case STUFD would be equal to 58_{10}. Although the assembler the reader is using may not allow multiplication ($*$) or division ($/$) in expressions, it is easy to see how these operators could be employed in creating useful variables generated automatically by the assembler, rather than *dynamically* by the program. Since this section is concerned with programming techniques, however, and since there is no uniformity among assemblers, even for the same microprocessor, not too many assembler-time tricks will be given. Use of pseudo-ops will also be kept to a minimum. The mnemonics used for the instructions are given in Appendices A–C. They are the symbols used by the microprocessor manufacturer and, in general, will correspond closely to the mnemonics used in microcomputer manufacturers' literature.

Moving Data

Data is moved in microcomputers a byte or sometimes 16 bits at a time. Data can be moved from cpu register to cpu register, from cpu register to memory, from memory to cpu register, and, with combinations of the above instructions, from memory to memory. Data is moved for various reasons. The entry point for most I/O data being input to the microcomputer is a cpu register. Since I/O data is usually many bytes long the data must be moved into an input buffer area in memory. For an output I/O operation the reverse is true. Data must be moved to an output buffer memory area from the cpu register. Temporary results must be moved to and from variables in memory to cpu registers. Data flags of different types must also be kept in flag words in memory. Constants must be moved into cpu registers to initialize index values or for comparisons.

The basic ground rules for data movement apply to other coding as well. Data should be kept in cpu registers whenever possible and memory references should be avoided. When a constant is to be loaded into a register one should always load the constant by immediate means whenever possible. The immediate load may save one or two memory locations if the constant is used only once, and execution of the immediate instruction is faster then a memory reference type of instruction. Variables should be assigned specific locations and should not be moved around. Data arranged in blocks, such as I/O buffers, should never be moved from one block of memory to another unless absolutely necessary. It takes milliseconds to move a block of 100 bytes from one block location to another. "Milliseconds" doesn't sound too expensive in terms of computer time, but repetitive moves of large blocks, as in sorting records, are among the slowest processing tasks in all computer systems. Alternative approaches to moving blocks are *lists* and *directories,* which are discussed in following chapters.

MOVING DATA—8080

The 8080 immediate instructions allow one to load an 8-bit immediate operand into any memory location or cpu register or to load a 16-bit immediate operand into register pairs B,C, D,E, H,L, or the stack pointer register. Let's look at the 8-bit case first. To move one byte of immediate data, the second byte of the instruction, into a cpu register the MVI R,DATA instruction is used.

```
CHARA EQU 0101
              .

              .
       MVI B,CHARA
```

Note that the value of octal 101, or an ASCII A, has been named CHARA, or character A. The equate takes up no memory location. The 8-bit immediate operand could have been moved to a memory location specified by the pointer or index value in the H,L registers by the instruction

```
       MVI M,CHARA
```

Sixteen-bit immediate values in bytes 2 and 3 of the immediate instruction can be moved into register pairs by the LXI RP,DATA instruction type. The RP mnemonic is replaced by B, D, H, or SP and the data value is a sixteen-bit value, many times representing a memory address, since B,C and D,E are index registers, H,L is the original memory pointer, and the stack pointer must hold a memory address of the stack. The instructions

```
       PETER  DS 10
       PAUL   DS 20
       MARY   DS 10
                .

                .
       LXI B,PETER
       LXI D,PAUL
       LXI H,MARY
       LXI SP,PETER
```

load B,C with the location of PETER, D,E with the location of PAUL, which is 10 bytes further on, H,L with the location of MARY, which is 30 bytes away from PETER, and SP with the stack area, which is location PETER. If PETER was at location 3000_8, the values loaded would have been 3000, 3012, 3024, and 3000, respectively. Needless to say, the register pairs are properly set up to be used as index registers or pointers to these areas. The following code would store 2 and 4 into locations PETER and PAUL.

```
MVI A,2
STAX B      INITIALIZE PETER AREA
MVI A,4
STAX D      INITIALIZE PAUL AREA
```

Of course, performing a LDAX B or LDAX D loads the 8-bit value at PETER or PAUL into the A register in the same fashion.

Another type of move instruction would be the MOV R,M or the MOV M,R instruction. Both use the H,L register pair as an address pointer. The following code moves 2 and 4 into the PETER and PAUL areas in a slightly different manner than the previous STAX code.

```
LXI H,PETER
MVI B,2
MOV M,B      INITIALIZE PETER AREA
LXI H, PAUL
MVI C,4
MOV M,C      INITIALIZE PAUL AREA
```

Data from the PETER and PAUL areas could be loaded into B and C by a MOV B,M and MOV C,M in the same manner.

Yet a third way to move data is the direct method where the LDA or STA instruction has a direct memory address in bytes 2 and 3 of the instruction. The code

```
MVI A,2
STA PETER     INITIALIZE PETER AREA
MVI A,4
STA PAUL      INITIALIZE PAUL AREA
```

accomplishes the same thing as the other two examples. In this case no pointer registers or index registers have to be set up. (Sigh! Which one to use . . .) Since the direct STA or LDA does not use index registers, these are normally the instructions that are most efficient. The exception would be if one or several of the register pairs were initialized to point to the appropriate areas anyway. Then an indexed or H,L move might be desired.

At times data must be moved from cpu register to cpu register. Since many instructions utilize the A register for arithmetic or logical instructions, the A register contents may have to be saved in another register, if one is available. MOV R1,R2 moves the contents of R2, the source register, to R1, the destination register. MOV B,C and MOV A,D move the contents of the C register to the B register and the contents of the D register to the A register, respectively.

These are the commonly used moves in the 8080. The remaining instructions that move data are more unique. SHLD and LHLD store and load the H,L registers from two consecutive memory locations, respectively. Since H,L are used in pointer type instructions where the register pair is used as an index register, SHLD and LHLD offer a convenient way to save the current contents of H,L, load a new pointer, and, at some future time, load the previous contents that were saved. SPHL transfers the contents of H,L to the SP register. XCHG swaps the contents of H,L and D,E. XTHL is also an exchange which swaps the contents of H,L and the top of stack memory locations. The stack pointer is not affected. More instructions that move data are discussed in the stack operations chapter.

In all the preceding instructions the cpu flags remain unaltered.

Clever programming tricks department: XRA A zeroes the A register and is one byte shorter and faster than the corresponding MVI A,O instruction.

MOVING DATA—6800

The index register or stack pointer register can be loaded or stored by LDX, LDS, STX, or STS. All addressing modes can be used in these instructions with the exception of the meaningless "inherent" and the immediate mode for the stores. Here, as in the 808 case, it is convenient to load a value immediately to save memory references and possibly some memory locations for the value. The following code loads the stack pointer with the top of stack and the index register with the beginning of a buffer area.

```
TSTCK EQU $A000
BUFR1 RMB 80          INPUT BUFFER
      .

      .
      LDX #BUFR1      POINT TO BUFFER
      LDS #TSTCK      RESET STACK POINTER
```

The immediate values #BUFR1 and #TSTCK are each 16 bits in length and occupy bytes 2 and 3 of the instructions. Similarly the STS and STX are used to save the contents of the stack pointer or index register.

```
      STX SAVEX       SAVE INDEX REG
      STS SAVES       SAVE STACK PNTR
```

If SAVEX is located in the page 0 area and can be resolved in 8 bits, the assembler automatically makes a direct instruction out of the STX. If SAVEX is out of page 0, then the STX must be an extended instruction of three bytes. This automatic *assembler-imposed* addressing relieves the programmer from explicitly identifying a location as page 0 or non-page 0. Can an index register be used in an LDX? There is no reason why not, as the cpu will calculate the effective address, pick up the 16-bit value to be loaded, and *then* load the index register to the new value. As an example of this, suppose that we have been using the index register to help in searching a table of buffer areas called BUFR1, BUFR2, . . . , BUFRN. The A accumulator holds the address of one of the buffer areas. When the corresponding BUFR address is found, the index register points to the location in the table which holds the buffer address. Executing the instruction

```
FOUND LDX   X    PICKUP BUFFER ADDRESS
```

loads the buffer address from the table into the index register, replacing the index value that points to the table entry.

The four instructions above affect some of the condition codes after execution. The H, I, and C condition codes are not affected. Overflow is cleared. N and Z are set to reflect the state of the sign bit and the zero/nonzero state of the index register or stack pointer. As in the implementation of many instructions among the three microprocessors, don't read any subtle meanings about why those condition code bits are changed. Note the fact and file it away.

Since the 6800 has only two general-purpose registers, the A and B accumulator, they are kept fairly busy and many operands must be saved in memory to be retrieved at a later time to free the accumulators for processing. LDAA, LDAB, STAA, and STAB load and store the A and B accumulators. All addressing modes but the meaningless inherent and immediate for the stores may be used. Operation is straightforward. As a refresher, if the index register contains 10_{10} and the code

```
STAA   TABLE,X    STORE NEXT VALUE IN TABLE
 .
 .
TABLE EQU   $100        NEXT GENERATION—PAGE 0
```

is executed, where will the contents of A be stored? If you have chosen TABLE+10_{10} (PAGE 0 $10A_{16}$) you are absolutely correct. LDA and STA affect the condition codes just as LDX, LDS, STX, and STS did. Overflow is cleared and the N and Z bits are set on the contents of the appropriate accumulator.

Transfer of data between cpu registers is handled by several inherent (one-byte) instructions. TAB, TBA, TXS, and TSX transfer data between A and B and between X and SP. The first letter stands for transfer, the next is the source register, and the last is the destination register. Eight bits are transferred between accumulators, and 16 bits between the index register and stack pointer. The condition codes are not affected for the TXS and TSX instructions, but are modified as in the preceding instructions for TAB and TBA. Two other inherent instructions clear either the A or B accumulator, CLRA and CLRB. The same instruction is used to clear a specified memory location, but the addressing may be only indexed or extended. The condition codes for all three CLRs are affected the same way. H and I remain unchanged, N, V, and C are cleared, and Z is set.

The last instruction of the 6800 move data types is the TPA instruction, an inherent instruction that transfers all of the condition codes to the *A* accumulator only. Bit positions 7 and 6 are set to one, while bit positions 5 through 0 hold H, I, N, Z, V, and C, respectively. The condition codes are not affected.

MOVING DATA—6502

The accumulator, X register, or Y register can be loaded or stored by instructions LDA, LDX, LDY, STA, STX, and STY. The addressing modes that can be used vary. All of the loads may be immediate, such as the code

```
JS      EQU  10
CPE     EQU  20
JCF     EQU  30
        .
        .
        .

BACH    LDA  #JS     NUMBER OF BYTES
        LDX  #CPE    START WITHIN BUFFER 1
        LDY  #JCF    START WITHIN BUFFER 2
```

The LDX and LDY instructions may be zero page or absolute addressing. However, when indexing is used, only the *other* index register may be used. In other words the instructions

```
        LDX  VALUE,Y    INITIALIZE INDEX
        LDY  VALUE,X
```

are valid, but

```
        LDX  VALUE,X    INITIALIZE INDEX
        LDY  VALUE,Y
```

are not. LDA, LDX, and LDY do not affect the C, I, D, V condition codes, but change N and Z according to the value loaded into the register. STA, STX, and STY operate much as one would expect. Only zero page, absolute, and zero page with the *other* index register are allowed for STX and STY. STA may use any memory reference addressing mode. Condition codes are not affected for the above three stores. The accumulator, X register, Y register, and stack pointer may be transferred to each other by the TAX, TAY, TSX, TXA, TXS, and TYA instructions, where the second letter is the source and the third letter is the destination register. N and Z are the only condition codes affected and are set according to the value transferred from the source register.

Examples of moving blocks of data will be provided in the chapter on loops. The above discussion is only a brief description of how data can be moved in 8-bit or 16-bit segments between cpu registers and memory.

Integer Arithmetic
Operations

The microcomputers discussed here allow easy implementation of the addition and subtraction of two 8-bit operands. None of the three microprocessors, however, have a multiply or divide instruction. The multiply and divide functions must be implemented by shifting or by special techniques which will be discussed.

The basic operations in adding or subtracting two bytes were discussed in Chapter 3. Negative numbers are represented in two's complement form with the sign bit set to a one and the range for 8 bits being -128 to -1. Zero is a positive number of 00000000_2. The range for positive values is 0 through $+127$. When two operands are added, there are three cases: addition of two positive numbers, addition of two negative numbers, and addition of a positive number and negative number. The maximum value in addition of two positive numbers is $+254$ while the maximum value for two negative numbers is -256. Both of these results would require a 9-bit signed number. An overflow condition exists when the result is -129 to -256 or $+128$ to $+254$, and the overflow flag is set in the cpu if the microprocessor has one. If the microprocessor does not have an overflow flag, the sign bit can be tested for overflow. Overflow exists when the sign bit flips after an add. Since overflow can never occur upon adding two unlike-signed operands the test would be made only for the case of adding two positive numbers or two negative numbers. Examples of overflow follow:

01111100	01111111	10000000	11111111
00000100	01111111	10000000	10000000
10000000	11111110	100000000	101111111

All three microcomputers have a carry flag that is set whenever there is a carry out of the most significant, or sign, bit of the result of an addition. The carry is useful as it permits double- and multiple-precision schemes that are discussed in the next chapter. In multiple-precision schemes the addition is really of two unsigned numbers that represent the lower order portion of a signed 16-bit number (or greater). In these cases the carry is the same as any other carry from a bit position with the exception that this carry can be easily tested and saved.

Subtraction is essentially the same as addition, as all three cases exist in the subtraction operands as did in the addition operands. The subtrahend is effectively two's complemented before the addition occurs, or a subtract mode bit is set in the arithmetic and logic unit of the cpu to effect a subtract rather than an add from the adder/subtractor logic.

In all cases the cpu flags representing carry, zero, and sign are set after the add or subtract has been performed. Any flags that are not arithmetic flags, such as the interrupt flag, are not affected. The arithmetic flags, of course, can now be tested to determine the results of the operation.

There are three general ways to multiply in software in microcomputers. The first is by *successive addition* of the multiplicand. The multiplicand is added to a partial sum the number of times equal to the multiplier. If, for instance, 45 was to be multiplied by 5 the partial sum would be zeroed, and 45 added 5 times to the partial sum. The second method is by shifting an operand to the left. Each left shift multiplies the original operand by two. Sometimes a combination of shifting and addition can be used. Multiplying by 10_{10} for example, can be implemented by shifting one bit position to the left, saving the result as TEMP1, shifting twice more, and then adding TEMP1 to the partial sum. To multiply 9 by 10, for example, we have

00001001	+9
00010010	+18 after left shift—save
00100100	+36 after left shift
01001000	+72 after left shift
00010010	add +18 saved
01011010	+90 = result

What has been done here is to factor 10 into 8+2, making the multiplication 9 × (8+2). Since both of the factors are powers of two, the subsequent multiplication by shifting and one add is easy to implement.

The first method of repetitive additions lends itself well to very small multipliers. The second method is hardly a general case, but works well for decimal conversions and other unique multiplies. The third method of multiplication discussed here is a general case multiply that will work for any two 8-bit operands. It is identical with the pencil-and-paper decimal multiply that the reader performs. (This is a very dangerous statement to make considering the proliferation of pocket calculators.) The method is illustrated below. Each bit of the multiplier is examined. If the bit is a zero, the partial result is shifted. If the bit is a one, the multiplicand is added to the partial result. The process continues until the last bit has been examined. Here is the multiply of 9_{10} and 40_{10}.

$$
\begin{array}{ll}
00001001 & +9 \\
00101000 & +40 \\
\hline
00000000 & \\
00000000 & \\
00000000 & \\
00001001 & \\
00000000 & \\
00001001 & \\
00000000 & \\
00000000 & \\
\hline
0000000101101000 & +360
\end{array}
$$

Note that the product is a 16-bit or double-precision number. Almost all software multiplications will produce 16-bit products. It's also apparent from the layout of the multiply that testing of the multiplier bits and shifting could have proceeded from the most significant bit first, with a shift in the opposite direction. Both approaches are used in multiply routines. An *unsigned* multiply routine is one in which both operands are considered positive; a *signed* multiply can be used with any combination of operands to produce a correctly signed result. In the latter an exclusive OR of the sign bits of the operands will give the sign of the product. The multiplicand and multiplier are then changed to their absolute values, multiplied by an unsigned multiply, and the product converted to the proper sign. For a 16-bit product, overflow can never occur. The worst cases of $+127$ by $+127$ and -128, by -128 produce $+16129$ and $+16384$, respectively, both of which can be held in a 16-bit signed value.

The techniques for division are somewhat similar to the techniques for multiplication. Division can be accomplished by *successive subtraction* of the divisor from the dividend *residue*. The count of the number of times the divisor can be subtracted before the residue goes to zero or below is the quotient. For example, suppose $+120$ was to be divided by $+20$. The process and the value of the running count is shown below:

01111000	+120	÷	00010100	+20

01111000	Dividend
11101100	Divisor, two's complemented for add
01100100	First residue, CNT=1
11101100	
01010000	Second residue, CNT =2
11101100	
00111100	Third residue, CNT=3
11101100	
00101000	Fourth residue, CNT=4
11101100	
00010100	Fifth residue, CNT=5
11101100	
00000000	Sixth residue, CNT=6
	Residue = 0, therefore quotient = 6

The second division method is used to divide by two. Shifting to the right divides by two for each shift. When this is done with a signed number, care must be taken to sign extend the most significant bit. An arithmetic shift to the right does this automatically. Dividing −120 by 8 involves three arithmetic right shifts:

10001000	−120 (two's complement)
11000100	First shift produces −60
11100010	Second shift produces −30
11110001	Third shift produces −15

Note that the sign bit is extended into the next bit position after each shift.

Just as in the case of the multiplies, the first division method works well for small divisors or for special cases, but not as a generic form of division. The usual software divide in microcomputers works with a 16-bit dividend and an 8-bit divisor, and is a *restoring* type of division similar to pencil-and-paper decimal division. The divisor is subtracted from the residue. If the result is negative, the residue is restored to the previous value and a zero is recorded as the quotient bit. If the result is positive, the result replaces the old residue and a one is recorded in the quotient bit. The residue is shifted up one bit position and the process continues. A detailed example of this type of divide is given in the programming algorithms section (Part 4) of this book. Once again, the divide may be an unsigned divide that operates on two positive operands, or it may be a signed divide. Generally the dividend is 16 bits, the divisor is 8 bits, and the quotient is 8 bits. An 8-bit remainder is also sometimes provided. Overflow is indeed possible for most divides. If the quotient is greater than $+127$ or less than -128 overflow has occurred and a software flag bit is generally set to indicate the overflow condition.

Double- and multiple-precision schemes that permit multiplies and divides of operands greater than 16 bits are discussed in the next chapter. Software routines to accomplish unsigned multiplies and unsigned divides are given in Part 4.

INTEGER ARITHMETIC—8080

The 8080 instructions permit two types of 8-bit adds and subtracts: adds or subtracts with carry and adds or subtracts without carry. The adds and subtracts with carry are used in double- or multiple-precision operations and will be discussed in the next chapter. The adds and subtracts without carry operate on the A register, that is, a second operand is added or subtracted from the operand in the A register and the result is placed in the A register. The cpu flags are set according to the results of the operation. The zero, sign, parity, carry, and auxiliary carry are affected. Operation is straightforward with no surprises. The second operand may be an immediate value, a memory operand, or a register operand. If it is a memory operand, then the H,L register pair points to the memory location. The following code computes the sum of two variables, one in memory and one in a cpu register, and adds a constant to the sum.

```
MOLLY DS    1
ME     DS    1
BABY   EQU   3
       .
       .
       .
       LXI   H,MOLLY    POINT TO MOLLY
       MOV   B,M        GET MOLLY
       .
       .
BLUEH  LXI   H,ME       POINT TO ME
       XRA   A          CLEAR A
       ADD   M          ME
       ADD   B          MOLLY AND ME
       ADI   BABY       MOLLY AND ME AND BABY MAKES 3
```

The code is deliberately inefficient to illustrate the three types of adds. Subtracts work in exactly the same fashion.

The 8080 also permits double-precision adds. They are mentioned here and not in the next section because they *are* implemented in the instruction set. In these the destination register is always the H,L register pair. B,C, D,E, H,L, or SP can be added to the contents of H,L with the result being placed into H,L. Only the carry flag is affected, with the other flags remaining the same. The add is an add of two 16-bit operands, with the sign bit considered to be in the most significant bit of the register pair. Here is a double-precision multiply by eight implemented by this type of instruction:

```
MULT8 LHLD OPRND     LOAD 16-BIT OPERAND
      DAD  H         OPERAND*2
      DAD  H         OPERAND*4
      DAD  H         OPERAND*8
        .
        .
        .
      OPRND DS  2    HOLDS DP OPERAND
```

Multiplication or division by shifting in the 8080 is complicated by the fact that all shifting is done by rotations. This means that the bit shifted out of the register will have to be cleared before rotating into the opposite bit position, and that negative operands will have to be sign-extended with a little additional code if a divide by two is to be performed. Here are two examples of a *logical* right and left shift performed on the 8080 to effect a divide by two and multiply by two. Each time the shift is performed the carry must be cleared to guarantee that a zero is shifted into the opposite end of the register. Clever programming tricks department: Executing an ANA A will clear the carry and leave the A register unchanged.

```
ANA A    CLEAR CARRY
RAL      MULTIPLY BY TWO
  .
  .
  .
ANA A    CLEAR CARRY
RAR      DIVIDE BY TWO
```

The above code works only with positive integers.

INTEGER ARITHMETIC—6800

The 6800 allows adds and subtracts with both accumulators with and without the current state of the carry. Adds and subtracts with the carry are discussed in the double-precision section of this book. The addend, or subtrahend, from memory or the immediate value, is added to the contents of either the A or B accumulator and the result goes to the accumulator. Flag bits H, N, Z, V, and C are affected. In this microprocessor overflow is set if arithmetic overflow results, as discussed previously. The two accumulators can be subtracted or added by SBA or ABA. In these instructions the contents of the B accumulator are added or subtracted from the contents of the A accumulator and the result is placed in the A accumulator.

Multiplication and division by shifting in the 6800 is easy because there is a true arithmetic shift implemented in either the ASL or ASR instruction. The shifting may be done either to a memory operand or to the contents of the A or B accumulator. The following code finds the average of four numbers and places the result in location AVAGE.

```
LDAA   NUM1     GET FIRST RESULT
ADAA   NUM2     ADD SECOND RESULT
ADAA   NUM3     ADD THIRD RESULT
ADAA   NUM4     ADD FOURTH RESULT
ASRA            DIVIDE BY 2
ASRA            DIVIDE BY 4
STAA   AVAGE    STORE RESULT
```

No check is made of overflow conditions. In practice this would have to be performed.

INTEGER ARITHMETIC—6502

The 6502 has adds and subtracts with carry *only,* so that if an add is to be performed without carry, the carry must first be cleared and if a subtract is to be performed without carry, the carry must be *set.* Once the carry is cleared or set the add or subtract presents no problems. An immediate or memory operand of 8 bits is added to or subtracted from the contents of the accumulator and the result is placed in the accumulator. The N, Z, V, and C condition codes are affected. Here, as in the 6800, an overflow condition can be checked easily by the V flag. The ADC and SBC instruction can be just about any type of addressing mode except for Z page Y and meaningless modes.

Multiplies by two present no problem in the 6502 since the so-called arithmetic shift left instruction shifts a zero into the least significant bit position. There is no arithmetic shift right, however. The LSR will perform a divide by two on positive operands with no problem, but additional code would be required to sign extend for negative operands. The following code duplicates the 6800 code above to find the average of four numbers. It works for positive results only.

```
LDA   NUM1     GET FIRST RESULT
CLC            CLEAR C
ADC   NUM2     ADD SECOND RESULT
CLC            CLEAR C
ADC   NUM3     ADD THIRD RESULT
CLC            CLEAR C
ADC   NUM4     ADD FOURTH RESULT
LSR            DIVIDE BY 2
LSR            DIVIDE BY 4
STA   AVAGE    STORE RESULT
```

15

Double- and Multiple-Precision Schemes

Single-precision applied to microcomputers usually means 8-bit operands, since the data bus and arithmetic and logic unit are both oriented toward 8-bit slices. A range of 0 through 255 is fine for setting up index values or for defining x,y coordinates on a video display, but it is generally useless for application programs that compute accounts receivables, determine frequencies for playing music, or perform scientific calculations. Even 16 bits, or double-precision quantities, may not be adequate for many applications, since a range of only +32767 to −32,768 is provided by 16-bit operands. Thirty-two bits provide a much more usable range for most applications, since the range is expanded to approximately ±4,294,967,296. In practice, precision much greater than 16 or 24 bits or so is usually handled by floating-point representation in microcomputers, which allows for *significance* of about seven decimal digits and a range of $1 \times 10^{\pm 99}$ or so. In this chapter we will discuss the implementation of double- and multiple-precision schemes that provide 16 or 24 bits, although there is no reason that the reader could not apply the principles to precisions of any number of bits.

Adding or subtracting in multiple precision basically involves saving the carry or borrow status from the next lower byte and adding it to the higher byte in the least significant bit position. As an example, suppose that two 16-bit double precision operands of +458 and +683 are to be added. The form of the operands is

$$0000000111001010 \quad + \ 458$$
$$0000001010101011 \quad + \ 683$$

where the *most significant* bit is the sign bit. This is true for any *n*-precision number; the most significant bit is the sign, and the previous sign bit position in the lower-order byte(s) are simply binary digits just as any other bit position. Since any add is generally of two 8-bit operands, the two numbers must be added in two steps. In the first step, the lower-order bytes are added and any carry out of the most significant bit position is saved:

$$
\begin{array}{r}
11001010 \\
10101011 \\
\hline
C \quad 01110101
\end{array}
$$

In the second step the higher-order two bytes are added, with any carry being added to the least significant bit position.

$$
\begin{array}{rl}
00000001 & \\
00000010 & \\
1 & \text{Carry from previous add} \\
\hline
00000100 &
\end{array}
$$

The two results are now merged into one 16-bit sum.

$$
0000010001110101 \qquad +1141
$$

This process of adding two bytes at a time, saving the carry, adding the next higher-order byte with the carry, saving the carry for the next add, and so forth, can be repeated for as many bytes as there are in the operands. Furthermore, the microprocessors discussed here have specific instructions to add the carry from the previous lower-order add, as we have seen.

Subtract works much the same way as an add, except that the carry, although still called a carry, is actually a borrow from the next higher-order byte. As an example, let's perform a subtract of +128 from +1024.

$$
\begin{array}{ll}
0000010000000000 & +1024 \\
0000000010000000 & +128
\end{array}
$$

$$
\begin{array}{ll}
00000000 & \text{Lower-order subtract by} \\
B \quad 10000000 & \quad \text{two's complement add} \\
\hline
10000000 &
\end{array}
$$

$$
\begin{array}{ll}
00000100 & \text{Higher-order subtract by} \\
00000000 & \quad \text{two's complement add} \\
-1 & \text{Borrow from lower-order subtract} \\
\hline
00000011 &
\end{array}
$$

$$
0000001110000000 \qquad +896 \text{ merged result}
$$

The subtract instructions would permit a lower-order borrow to propagate into the next higher-order bit positions similarly to the add with carry instructions.

The carry to higher-order bit positions must be considered not only in addition and subtraction of multiple-precision numbers. If a multiple-precision number were to be negated or two's complemented, any carry to higher-order bytes must be added in by the same process. If +1024 is to be negated, the two's complement is first taken of the low-order byte:

$$00000000 \qquad \text{Low-order byte of } 0000010000000000$$

$$11111111$$
$$+1$$

C ⤏ $\overline{00000000}$ Two's complement of low-order byte

Then the *one's* complement is taken of the high-order byte and any carry is added in.

$$00000100 \qquad \text{High-order byte of } 0000010000000000$$

| 11111011 | One's complement of high-order byte |
| +1 | Carry from low-order byte |

11111100   Result

1111110000000000   −1024 merged result

This process could be repeated for a number of any precision. An explicit test would have to be made for the carry, as none of the microprocessors have a "complement with carry" instruction. This is done by performing a one's complement by the appropriate instruction, testing a flag indicating a carry from the low-order complement, and adding one to the one's complemented value if the flag is set.

Double-precision and multiple-precision multiplication and division are quite a bit more complicated than addition and subtraction. A multiply by repeated additions or a divide by repeated subtractions is one way to implement a multiple-precision multiply and divide. In this method, of course, the additions and subtractions are multiple-precision, using the techniques discussed above. Multiplication or division by two or by any number that can be factored into powers of two is also possible by performing double- or multiple-precision shifts. The shifts operate as one would expect, with the shifted bit going into the carry flag and any previous carry being shifted into the vacated bit position. Sign extension on a right shift for a divide is performed by extending the sign in the most significant byte by whatever means are available for single-byte sign extension.

The usual method for implementing a double-precision multiply takes advantage of the fact that a double-precision number can be expressed as $B + (A \times 256)$. The B portion is the low-order byte value while A is the high-order byte, and it can easily be seen that any double-precision number can be resolved in this form, as, for example, $+683$:

$$
\begin{aligned}
0000001010101011 \text{ or } +683 &= (00000010 \times 256) + 10101011 \\
&= \quad (2 \times 256) \quad + \quad 171 \\
&= \quad \quad 512 \quad \quad + \quad 171 \\
&= 683
\end{aligned}
$$

Multiplication of two double-precision operands is achieved by the expansion of $(A + B) \times (C + D)$ where B and D are the low-order bytes of each operand, and A and C are the high-order bytes. The factor of 256 for A and C has been made implicit for clarity. Now,

$$
\begin{aligned}
(A + B) \times (C + D) = \ &B \times D \\
&+ B \times C \times 256 \\
&+ D \times A \times 256 \\
&+ A \times C \times 65{,}536
\end{aligned}
$$

Four single-precision multiplies of $A \times C, A \times D, B \times C,$ and $B \times D$ are performed and the results of each are saved. The results are now merged by multiple-precision adds of four bytes, as the product can never exceed four bytes, except in one case, the multiplication of $-32{,}768$ by itself. The arrangement of the adds is determined by the factor of 1, 256, or 65,536 for each of the four products. If the four bytes of the product are numbered 3, 2, 1, and 0 from left to right, then all four bytes are cleared, the BD product is added to bytes 1 and 0 in double-precision, the BC product is added to bytes 2 and 1 of the result, the DA product is added to bytes 2 and 1 of that result, and the AC product is added to bytes 3 and 2 to produce the final product.

Division of multiple-precision numbers in the generic form is the most awkward of any of the multiple-precision operations, causing stout-hearted microcomputer programmers to throw up their hands in despair. Probably the best way to implement a divide involving a dividend of more than two bytes is to emulate a single-precision divide, where a subtract of the divisor is done, the result tested, a restore and a 0 or no restore and a 1 is put into the quotient, and the process is repeated for the $n - 1$ bits of the dividend. Only $n - 1$ iterations are usually required because the subtraction, test, and restore do not have to be done to the sign bit of the dividend. This process would involve multiple-precision subtracts and adds of the divisor to the dividend, multiple-byte shifts of the partial quotient, and quite a bit of data shuffling from cpu registers to memory storage and back. For those readers who think that this is a cop-out, it most certainly is. A divide of a two-byte dividend and one-byte divisor is described in Part 4 of this book, but if more precision is required, the reader is advised to consult listings of manufacturers' software or other programming reference materials.

MULTIPLE PRECISION—8080

As described in the previous chapter, the 8080 has a built-in double-precision add in the form of the DAD instructions. The DAD allows a series of double-precision adds where the multiple-precision operands are multiples of two bytes long. Take the following example, where there are two four-byte operands in locations FOUR1 and FOUR2 which must be added to produce a sum that is to be placed in FOURS.

```
FOUR1   DS    4     HOLDS QUAD PRECISION NO 1
FOUR2   DS    4     HOLDS QUAD PRECISION NO 2
        .
        .
QUADA   LHLD  FOUR1+2   GET TWO LS BYTES
        XCHG            FOUR1+2 TO D,E
        LHLD  FOUR2+2   GET TWO LS BYTES
        DAD   D         FIND LS RESULT
        SHLD  FOURS+2   STORE LS RESULT
        LHLD  FOUR1     GET TWO MS BYTES
        JNC   BYPAS     JUMP IF NO CARRY
        INX   H         DOUBLE PRECISION BUMP
BYPAS   XCHG            FOUR1 TO D,E
        LHLD  FOUR2     GET 2 MS BYTES
        DAD   D         FIND MS RESULT
        SHLD  FOURS     STORE MS RESULT
        .
        .
FOURS   DS    4         HOLDS QUAD PRECISION RESULT
```

In the general case the 8080 performs multiple-precision adds and subtracts by the ACI, ADC, SBI, and SBB instructions in conjunction with the normal adds and subtracts. The ACI, ADC, SBI, and SBB instructions add in a carry or subtract a borrow in addition to the immediate, memory, or register operand. To perform a double-precision subtract, for example, the following code would be used:

```
LDA   OP2+1   GET LS BYTE OF ARG 2
MOV   B,A     MOVE TO B
LDA   OP1+1   GET LS BYTE OF ARG 2
SUB   B       A—B
STA   RES+1   STORE LS BYTE OF RESULT
LDA   OP2     GET MS BYTE OF ARG 2
MOV   B,A     MOVE TO B
LDA   OP1     GET MS BYTE OF ARG 1
SBB   B       A—B WITH BORROW
```

```
         STA    RES      STORE MS BYTE OF RESULT
          .
          .
 OP1    DS    2        DP ARG 1
 OP2    DS    2        DP ARG 2
 RES    DS    2        DP RESULT
```

Multiple-precision shifting for repeated additions or subtractions to effect multiplies or divides are relatively easy to do on the 8080. An example of a 32-bit shift using four registers could be implemented as follows. The four-byte number to be shifted is in B,C,D,E and a right shift is required.

```
SHFT4   ANA    A      CLEAR CARRY
        MOV    A,B
        RAR           SHIFT B
        MOV    B,A
        MOV    A,C
        RAR           SHIFT C
        MOV    C,A
        MOV    A,D
        RAR           SHIFT D
        MOV    D,A
        MOV    A,E
        RAR           SHIFT E
        MOV    E,A
```

MULTIPLE PRECISION—6800

The 6800 has two instructions, ADC and SBC, that permit an add or subtract with carry. Any addressing mode is permitted and the add or subtract can be performed on the contents of the A or B accumulators by an immediate or memory operand, but not by the contents of the other accumulator. An example of a double-precision add with the result held in accumulators A and B would be as follows:

```
ARG1    RMB    2      DP ARGUMENT 1
ARG2    RMB    2      DP ARGUMENT 2
         .
         .
        LDAB   ARG1+1  LS BYTE IN B
        LDAA   ARG1    MS BYTE IN A
        ADDB   ARG2+1  GET LS BYTE OF RESULT
        ADCA   ARG2    ADD CARRY FOR MS BYTE
```

As the 6800 has a true arithmetic shift, multiple-precision right shifting to implement division by two is easy. Also, the shifts, whether arithmetic or logical, may be performed on memory operands, so that one is not forced to shift a cpu register, store the result, load the next portion, shift and store, and so forth, Shifting a four-byte multiple-precision operand in memory location LOCUS is accomplished by the following code:

```
SHIFT  LSR   LOCUS      SET CARRY
       ROR   LOCUS+1    PROPAGATE CARRY
       ROR   LOCUS+2    HERE TOO
       ROR   LOCUS+3    HERE TOO
```

MULTIPLE PRECISION—6502

Multiple-precision adds or subtracts in the 6502 use the same ADC and SBC instructions that are used in single-precision operations. The carry is not changed for the high-order adds and subtracts, of course. An example of the subtraction of two triple-precision operands in OP1 and OP2 with the result going to RES follows:

```
OP1   RMB   3      TRIPLE PREC ARG 1
OP2   RMB   3      TRIPLE PREC ARG 2
RES   RMB   3      TRIPLE PREC RESULT
      .
      .
      SEC          SET CARRY
      LDA   OP1+2  GET LS BYTE
      SBC   OP2+2  LS RESULT
      STA   RES+2  STORE LS RESULT
      LDA   OP1+1
      SBC   OP2+1
      STA   RES+1  STORE NEXT RESULT
      LDA   OP1
      SBC   OP2
      STA   RES    STORE MS RESULT
```

Shifting operations in the 6502 for purposes of multiplication or division by two are similar to the 6800. Either the accumulator or a memory operand can be shifted. A true arithmetic right shift cannot be performed, however, and sign extension of negative multiple-precision operands must be accomplished by some extra coding.

Branching, Loops, and Indexing

The three microprocessors discussed have taken some written abuse from the author for various quirks in the instruction set, but there is one area in which kudos are deserved. This is the implementation of branch and jump instructions. The conditional and unconditional branches and jumps are very powerful in comparison to many of the popular minicomputers. The ability to branch conditionally on carry or no carry, zero or nonzero, positive and negative, and other conditions eliminates much code that would be used to perform these tests in other machines.

Up to this point in the book we have not used conditional branching to any extent in the examples. Some of the preceding code could have been shortened by using the techniques of indexing, loops, and conditional branching. The basic structure for indexing is the *loop,* whose etymology lies buried somewhere in the archives of computers. Every loop has an initialization portion, main body, and termination/ testing portion. Using an example of a 6502 loop a simple loop would be represented by

```
        LDX  #20     SETUP INDEX TO 20
LOOP    DEX          DECREMENT BY 1
        BNE  LOOP     GO IF NOT ZERO
NEXT    .
        .
```

The first instruction loads an index register with the immediate value of 20. This is the initialization portion. The next instruction decrements the count in the index register by one. This is the main body.

The last instruction tests the state of the zero (Z) cpu flag. If the flag is nonzero, indicating that the last decrement resulted in a non-zero value in the index register, then a branch is made back to the location LOOP, where the decrement is repeated. The last instruction is the testing/termination portion. This short loop would be executed twenty times, until the count in index register X was decremented down to zero, at which point the conditional branch would not be made and the instruction at NEXT would be executed.

An example of a loop the author has written many times is shown below.

```
MOBUS   LDX   #20      SETUP INDEX TO 20
        DEX            DECREMENT BY 1
        BNE   MOBUS    GO IF NOT ZERO
        .
        .
```

This is an example of an endless loop, as the initialization portion is continually reentered and the index count can never reach zero. It alternates between 20_{10} and 19_{10}.

In the two examples above, nothing really much is accomplished in the loop. The only thing the first loop would be used for is perhaps as a timing loop. The total time of the loop—initialization, main body, and testing—would be one instruction time for the initialization and two times 20 instruction times for the main body and testing, or about 41 instruction times, corresponding to about 0.2 millisecond. The main body of the loop generally has more processing and sometimes a great deal of processing since as much code as required can be inserted into the main body. A brief example of this would be the following loop, which searches a table of characters looking for an ASCII A. The table is 20 characters long, so if the A is not found after 20 characters, the search is ended. If the A is found a conditional branch is made to location FND.

```
        LDY   #0         INDEX FOR TABLE START
        LDX   #20        SETUP INDEX TO 20 **
LOOP    LDA   TABLE,Y    GET NEXT CHARACTER
        CMP   #'A        IS IT AN A?
        BEQ   FND        GO IF IT IS
        INY              INCREMENT BY ONE
        DEX              DECREMENT BY ONE **
        BNE   LOOP       GO IF NOT TABLE END **
        .
        .
TABLE   RMB   20
```

The original code of the loop is marked with asterisks. The other code is additional processing within the loop. Note that there are now two ways to end the loop, either by searching through the entire table or by finding the character before the end of the table. There is no reason why there cannot be many ways to conditional branch out of the loop. The important point, however, is that somewhere there must be a terminating condition to end the loop.

The above example illustrates another important point. Since the 6502 has two index registers, one of them was used to count the number of times through the loop, while the other was used to *index through a table* two different types of indexing operations. The first character loaded was from location TABLE. As the Y index was incremented, the next character loaded was from TABLE+1, the next from TABLE+2, and so on. This is a common type of operation in almost any program.

Not only is a series of loops possible, but there may be loops within loops, or *nested* loops, another common operation within many programs. A simple two-level timing loop using the convenient 6502 index registers is shown below.

```
        LDY   VAR1      CONSTANT 1
LOPO    LDX   VAR2      CONSTANT 2
LOPI    DEX             INNER LOOP
        BNE   LOPI      GO TO INNER LOOP
        DEY             OUTER LOOP
        BNE   LOPO      GO TO OUTER LOOP
        .
        .
VAR1    RMB   1         TIME OF OUTER LOOP
VAR2    RMB   1         TIME OF INNER LOOP
```

Here two variables VAR1 and VAR2 are used to establish the starting index values for the two registers. Variable times from about 30 microseconds to about 0.6 second can be achieved by putting in different values for the variables. Here, just as in the one-level loop, the nested loops may have any amount of processing within them, and various exits may be made by conditional branches under certain conditions, changing the timing loops into two-level processing loops. Any number of nested loops is possible.

Lest this discussion gives the wrong impression, conditional branches are not used only in loops. They are far more often used in simply determining alternate paths in the program to be taken depending upon various conditions. Many times these conditions are held in software flags or variables inside the program. In a lot of cases these flags indicate yes or no conditions, but in other cases more states are used to reflect a number of different things. If the flag is a binary 1 or zero, it is easily checked by a load or by a load and compare which sets the Z flag to a one or zero and permits a conditional branch on Z or non-Z. If the flag holds a number of states a comparison is done to determine the state with a subsequent branch on equal (or zero). A typical set of flags are given here.

```
MODE    DS    1    MODE FLAG-HOLDS PASS #, 0 — 4
TTY     DS    1    0=TTY, 1=NO TTY
DFLT    DS    1    0=DEFAULT OPTIONS, 1=USER-SELECT
NOSP    DS    1    0=SPACE, 1 = NO SPACE
MSPF    DC    1    0=SYSTEM PAID FOR, 1 = NOT
```

A question that arises sometimes when writing programs is when to use a loop and when to use straight-line coding. In general, a loop should be used whenever the overhead of initializing the loop and testing for the end of the loop is small in comparison to the average total time through the loop. Another factor is the amount of storage required. The loop approach is almost always smaller in size than the equivalent straight-line coding. A third factor is timing. If one is to do a great deal of processing and that processing must be done as rapidly as possible, then straight-line coding is called for. This is not usually the case with many programs.

Many examples of the use of loop will be given in the following chapters as loops are just naturally a good way to implement certain things.

BRANCHING, LOOPS, INDEXING—8080

All of the 8080 registers *could* be used as index registers, since each as the ability to be incremented or decremented. However, A is used for arithmetical functions, logical functions, and shifting, and it is usually reserved for this type of processing. In addition, the register pairs B,C, D,E, and H,L can be incremented and decremented as double-precision index values. Also, LDAX and STAX use B,C and D,E as index pointer registers, so the logical grouping is three sets of double-precision index registers or six registers that may be used as single-precision index registers, or any combination of the two. Multiple indexing can easily be implemented on the 8080 as is shown in the following example, in which B holds a table size, and H,L points to the current entry in the table. The code computes the *checksum* of all of the entries in the table by adding each byte to a checksum value.

```
        MVI    B,25        25 ENTRIES IN TABLE
        LXI    H,TABLE     ADDRESS OF TABLE
        XRA    A           ZERO A
LOOP    ADD    M           ADD NEXT ENTRY
        INX    H           POINT TO NEXT ENTRY
        DCR    B           DECREMENT INDEX COUNT
```

```
        JNZ   LOOP        GO IF NOT DONE
          .
          .
   TABLE  DS    25        TABLE OF VALUES
```

A caution to be observed when working with the 8080 registers is that decrements or increments of register pairs *do not* change the condition codes. Therefore it is not valid to test for a zero or other condition after adjusting the index value by a DCX RP or INX RP instruction. A compare must be done to one or sometimes both registers to determine if the terminating condition has been reached. Decrements and increments done by DCR and INR change the Z, S, P, and AC condition codes as expected. In addition, a memory location can be used as an index value by the use of INR M or DCR M. The condition codes change in the same fashion as if a register was being used.

Another caution to be observed is that the 8080 does not change the condition codes when an LDA, LDAX, or MOV is performed. This means that if a conditional branch is to be made on the status of a software flag, that flag must be loaded into a register and then tested by some means. If the A register is used, an ANA A could be used. As a testing alternative, an RAR instruction could be used for flags that are zero or one. The least significant bit is shifted into the carry in this case, and a subsequent JC or JNC could be made. The same method would apply for the most significant bit, which could be tested by an RLC instruction. Many times a flag word can do double duty for two flags by using the most significant and least significant bits for two separate flags, if those bits are easily tested as they are in this case. Be certain to set or reset the flags properly, however, by using ORs, ANDs, and exclusive ORs.

```
        To set the msb of a double-flag word:
   GETFL  LDA    FLAG1      GET FLAG
          ORI    0200       SET MSB FLAG
            .


        To set the lsb of a double-flag word:
   GETFL  LDA    FLAG1      GET FLAG
          ORI    1          SET LSB FLAG
            .


        To reset the msb of a double-flag word:
   GETFL  LDA    FLAG1      GET FLAG
          ANI    0177       RESET FLAG
            .
```

To reset the lsb of a double-flag word:

```
GETFL   LDA     FLAG1       GET FLAG
        ANI     0376        RESET FLAG
```

Other methods of testing multiple flags are discussed in Chapter 21.

BRANCHING, LOOPS, INDEXING—6800

The 6800, of course, has one register set aside for indexing. The index register is added to the value of the displacement field in the second byte of an indexing type instruction to form the effective address. Because the index register is a 16-bit register it can be used to point to any memory location allowing the 6800 to index through memory locations easily. There is no reason, however, that the A accumulator, B accumulator, or a memory location cannot be used to hold an index value of 0 through 255 which can be used as an index count. The two accumulators can be incremented and decremented, as can the memory location, and the condition codes are set after each adjustment.

An example of another type of checksum using the index register and an index count in the B accumulator is provided below. The checksum in this case is formed by taking the exclusive OR of each of the bytes in a given area.

```
        LDX #TABLE      POINT TO TABLE
        CLRA            ZERO A
        LDAB #-25       INDEX COUNT
LOOP    ADDA X          ADD NEXT BYTE
        INX
        INCB            BUMP INDEX COUNT
        BMI LOOP        GO IF NOT 25 TIMES
        .
        .
TABLE   RMB 25          TABLE OF VALUES
```

There are several interesting things that appear in this code. First of all, a negative value is used as the index count, and this value is incremented to zero. Secondly, the conditional branch is made as long as the count is negative, illustrating that the conditional branch may be made on zero, crossing zero to a minus count, or crossing zero to a plus count.

Testing software flags in the 6800 is facilitated by the TST instruction, which is specifically set up for that purpose. The N and Z bits of the condition codes are set after the TST to reflect the sign and zero status of a specified memory operand or the contents of one of the accumulators. A software flag in memory can therefore be tested without loading it into the accumulator in one instruction.

Naturally the flags are set for compares and during arithmetic, increment, and decrement instructions as well as flags for conditional branches can also be tested in this fashion.

BRANCHING, LOOPS, INDEXING—6502

The 6502 uses a slightly different form of indexing than the 6800. The index registers are 8 bits long and the displacement fields in ABS,X and ABS,Y instructions are 16 bits long to compensate for the index register length. Effective addresses to address any memory location can still be formed either by Z PAGE X, Z PAGE Y, ABS,X, ABS,Y, (IND,X), or (IND),Y addressing. Indexing through memory must be done in 256-byte chunks, however, as the current value in an index register will vary from 0 through 255. This is usually no detriment, as many tables are less than 256 bytes long. Here is an example that zeroes a 768-byte area.

```
        LDX   #255          INITIALIZE INDEX
        LDA   #0
LOOP    STA   TABLE,X        ZERO FIRST 256 BYTES
        STA   TABLE+256,X        SECOND
        STA   TABLE+512,X        THIRD
        DEX                  ZERO FROM 255 TO 0
        BPL   LOOP           GO IF 255 THROUGH 0
        .
        .
TABLE   RMB   768            TABLE OF VALUES
```

The 6502 does not have a test instruction like the 6800, but does set the condition flags on loads, enabling a conditional branch on N or Z. Memory flags can also be tested by shift instructions which would set the carry in addition to N and Z, but would leave the flag altered.

Subroutines

A subroutine is a set of instructions, varying from several to hundreds or thousands, that can be utilized at different points in a program by CALLs. The idea behind the subroutine is that a set of instructions can be written once in a program rather than many times. This saves memory at the expense of execution of a few more instructions. Suppose, for example, that some code was written to find the square root of a number. If the square roots of ten variables were required at ten separate places in the program the same code could be written in those ten separate places. The alternative would be to write the code once, in a subroutine, and CALL that subroutine at the ten points in the program at which the square root had to be calculated. At the point of the CALL the accumulator might hold the number whose square root was to be found. The CALL would transfer the program to the address of the subroutine, the return address would be pushed into the stack automatically, the subroutine's code would be executed, and at the completion of the subroutine a return from subroutine instruction would be executed which would pop the return address from the stack and transfer control back to the instruction after the call. The accumulator would contain the square root of the number. The CALLs are called CALLs on the 8080, branch or jump to subroutines on the 6800, and jump to subroutine on the 6502. The return from subroutine is called return on the 8080, return from subroutine on the 6800, and return from subroutine on the 6502.

The return address is sometimes called the *link* on other computers. Formerly it was the programmer's responsibility to save the link and properly make the return at the end of the subroutine by an indexed or indirect jump. The microprocessor manufacturers have implemented these required actions in the call and return from subroutine instructions, realizing that these are standard actions to be taken for subroutines. Let's hear it for the microprocessor manufacturers!

In each subroutine there are a certain number of *arguments* that must be passed from the calling program to the subroutine to operate upon. The number of arguments would vary from none, as, for example, in a subroutine whose purpose is to perform a line feed on a Teletype, to many, as in a subroutine that writes a specified character to vdt screen coordinate X,Y, and then delays n microseconds. In the latter example, the character, X, Y, and n are all parameters that would be *passed* to the subroutine as arguments.

The method of passing arguments to a certain extent depends upon the type of microprocessor, but also is related to the type of programming being done. The 8080 has a large number of cpu registers, and it may be very feasible to hold the arguments in two or three registers, depending upon the precision and number of arguments. The 6800 and 6502 have fewer cpu registers and it probably is not always feasible to hold all the arguments in registers. Alternative ways to pass arguments are to group the arguments somewhere in memory with one of the cpu registers pointing to the starting memory location. Page 0 is a good place to put the arguments in the case of the 6502, as only 8 bits can be held in the index registers. Another possibility is to push the arguments into the stack before the jump to subroutine is made. This is somewhat less desirable than the argument in memory approach, as the subroutine now has to increment the stack pointer past the return address to pick up the arguments, put the return address in the proper place for the return from subroutine, and in general manipulate the stack in a way in which it was not meant to be used.

There are two general considerations when using subroutines that should be emphasized: saving registers and reentrancy. When a subroutine makes use of cpu registers, the calling program should be aware of this and either expect a return from the subroutine with the registers destroyed or push the registers into the stack before the call is made. An alternative approach is to have the subroutine push the registers that can be saved and restore them prior to the return. In any event, some comments should be put in the listings about which registers carry parameters, which are destroyed, and which are saved to remind the programmer.

The second consideration is reentrancy. If your system has interrupts this will be important to you. If a subroutine is shared by software that is not part of interrupt processing and software that *is* part of interrupt processing it may be possible to have data erroneously modified by the action of the interrupt processing. Take, for example, a subroutine that performs an *n*-bit shift of data in the accumulator. In this 6800 example, the number to be shifted is in the A register and *n* is in the index register. The subroutine temporarily stores the partial result in a memory location inside the program called TEMP1. If the interrupts are enabled at that point and, if an interrupt occurs, an interrupt processing routine is entered. If that interrupt processing routine includes as part of the processing calling the shift subroutine, it will be *reentered*. If it is reentered, it will use TEMP1 for the new value to be shifted, destroying the old value. When the interrupt processing is done, the return from interrupt causes a return to the interrupted instruction, somewhere within the shift subroutine. TEMP1 will be utilized by the subroutine, but it will contain an erroneous value because of the reentrancy.

```
              SHIFTN  . . .              SHIFT N PLACES SR
                      .
                      .
                      STA    TEMP1       TEMPORARY STORAGE
                      .
INTERRUPT————→        .
                      .
                      LDA    TEMP1       PICKUP SAVED RESULT
                      RET                RETURN
              TEMP1   DS     1           TEMPORARY STORAGE FOR SR
```

  There are several ways around this problem. The easiest is to use the stack for temporary storage, doing a push in place of the STA and a pull in place of the LDA. If reentrancy occurs a different stack location is used and the old data is saved. Another method is to turn off the interrupts whenever memory is used as storage. They must be off, however, for the entire time the memory storage area is used. The third method involves using a separate storage area for each system task. The calling task would then tell the subroutine what area to use for temporary storage. There are other methods, but by far the easiest and probably best method for microcomputers is to use the stack.

  Another important point, which cannot be emphasized too strongly, is that all subroutines that use the stack must properly maintain the stack pointer. If the subroutine does five pushes for temporary storage, there *must be* five pulls, or the stack pointer must be *adjusted* to the stack address it was pointing at when the subroutine was entered. It is very easy to get confused about the current level when there are multiple exit points from the subroutine and the stack has been used also. Each entry point must be set up so that the stack level on return from subroutine corresponds to the stack level on subroutine entry.

Just as loops may be nested to any number of levels, subroutines can also be nested to (just about) any number of levels. Since the return addresses are saved in the stack area, there are no return problems as long as the same number of return from subroutines as calls are made, and as long as the same number of pushes as pops (pulls) are made if the stack is used for temporary storage. The qualifier in the first statement was made because the stack *is* a finite size and it *is* possible to make enough calls or pushes to overflow the stack and start storing in a program area.

Just as in the case of loops versus in-line coding, there are times to use subroutines and times not to. Obviously if only one call is made to a given subroutine in the entire program, the subroutine could be incorporated as in-line code at no loss in storage. Also, if the subroutine is one that does not lend itself to a generic form, that is, if it takes too much overhead to find out the proper processing for the given arguments or simply requires too many arguments, it may be time to abandon the generic form and construct a special case for each occurrence of the processing in the program. Generally, though, many routines can be subroutinized to the programmer's advantage, both in reduction in memory used and in software modularity.

SUBROUTINES—8080

The 8080 can call subroutines either unconditionally by the call instruction, or conditionally by the call on carry, minus, no carry, no zero, positive, parity even, parity odd, or call on zero instructions (CC, CM, CNC, CNZ, CP, CPE, CPO, or CZ). All calls have the same result if the condition is met. The current contents of the program counter is pushed into the stack and a jump is made to the effective address, which is in bytes 2 and 3 of the instruction. A return from subroutine is also conditional or unconditional. The RET is an unconditional return and the RC, RM, RNC, RNZ, RP, RPE, RPO, and RZ conditional returns. The following illustrates a square-root routine that finds the integer portion of the square root of an 8-bit number. A call to SQRT is made with the square in the A register. The subroutine returns with the contents of A and C destroyed and the integer square root in the B register. If the square is zero, a return is immediately made.

```
KUKLA   LDA    SQ1      LOAD SQUARE 1
        CALL   SQRT     FIND SQUARE RT
        STA    SQR1      AND STORE
FRAN    LDA    SQ2      LOAD SQUARE 2
        CALL   SQRT     FIND SQUARE RT
        STA    SQR2      AND STORE
```

```
OLLIE    LDA    SQ3      LOAD SQUARE 3
         CALL   SQRT     FIND SQUARE RT
         STA    SQR3      AND STORE
          .
          .
          .
SQRT     MVI    B,O      INITIALIZE SQ RT
         CPI    O
         RZ              RETURN IF SQ = 0
         MVI    C,1      INITIALIZE ODD NUMBERS
LOOP     SUB    C        SUBTRACT NEXT ODD NUMBER
         RZ              RETURN IF 0
         RM              RETURN IF MINUS
         INR    B        BUMP SQUARE ROOT COUNT
         INR    C        GET NEXT ODD NUMBER
         INR    C
         JMP    LOOP     GO FOR NEXT SUBTRACT
```

By the way, this routine is based on the fact that the nth perfect square is the sum of the first n odd numbers. For example, the third perfect square, 9, is the sum of the first three odd numbers, $1+3+5 = 9$. This routine capitalizes on that fact to find the integer portion of the square root of squares from 0 through 127, and it serves to illustrate the use of calls and conditional and unconditional returns.

SUBROUTINES—6800

The call instruction in the 6800 is either JSR or BSR. Their difference is in the addressing modes employed. BSR, Branch to Subroutine, uses only relative addressing as do the other types of branches. This means that the subroutine must be somewhere within the floating page of the current instruction. The return within the subroutine may be anywhere, as the return from subroutines RTS uses the link address saved in the stack. JSR, Jump to Subroutine, uses indexed or extended addressing and can therefore be used to jump to any subroutine from any current location. Both BSR and JSR have the same action as far as the stack is concerned, transferring the link to the stack and decrementing the stack pointer. RTS does not affect the condition codes, which means that the condition codes involved in the subroutine processing could be maintained as special flags. The following routines use overflow for what it is intended—an overflow flag for a double-precision subroutine. Upon entry the index register points to the first operand with the A,B accumulators holding the second operand. The result of the add is left in A,B. If overflow occurs, the flag is set upon return.

```
DPADD    INX             POINT TO LS OPERAND
         ADDB   X        FIND LS RESULT
```

```
DEX           CARRY NOT AFFECTED
ADCA    X     FIND MS RESULT
RTS           C,O SET OR RESET
```

SUBROUTINES—6502

The 6502 has only one jump to subroutine: JSR. It uses only absolute addressing. The return from subroutine is made via the RTS instruction. The stack actions are as expected and condition codes are not changed when the RTS is executed.

18

Stack Operations

As described in previous chapters, the stack in the three microprocessors under discussion is a very convenient feature for the programmer, providing a large storage area that is not affected by interrupt processing, and being a means to automatically save the environment during interrupt processing. There are no great problems associated with stack use, but there are several common sense precautions to take.

The stack area itself can be located in any area of memory that will not be used by the program, except for the case of the 6502, which uses the second page of memory as a stack area (100_{16}–$1FF_{16}$). The stack area must be large enough for the types of programs being run. If there are many nested subroutines and a lot of use of the stack as a temporary storage, then the stack area must be correspondingly larger. In general, though, there is usually a great deal of memory available for the stack, and stack overflow will be no problem except in the smallest microcomputer systems.

The first action to take upon entry to a program must be stack initialization. If interrupts are being used this is especially true, as processing an interrupt before the stack is initialized will result in erroneously storing data in a random part of memory as a result of the automatic interrupt action. The stack pointer can usually be loaded with a literal (immediate) value that represents the top of stack. Note that the stack area "builds down," that is, as items are pushed into the stack, lower and lower memory locations are used. When the stack pointer is loaded it is loaded with a value that truly represents the *top* of stack, if the reader pictures memory as a rectangle in which the bottom represents memory location 0 and the top represents the highest-valued memory location in the system.

If stack overflow should result either because of a coding error that doesn't maintain the stack pointer properly or because the stack area is too small, there will be no automatic indication of the fault. (On some larger computers stack overflow or *underflow* results in an automatic fault interrupt.) In the 8080 or 6800 the program may bomb as a result of writing into the program area, or the problem may manifest itself in a slightly more subtle way that takes some time to be discovered. In the 6502, the stack will simply be reset to about the top of stack, as the stack pointer is a 9-bit register with the msb set to 1; changing the stack level can never result in a current stack location other than 100_{16} through $1FF_{16}$. If stack underflow results (too many pulls or pops), the same type of errors occur as erroneous data is read or subsequent pushes overwrite non-stack locations.

All of the microprocessors discussed here have instructions to push 8 bits or 16 bits of data into the stack and to pull data from the stack. Instructions are included to update the stack pointer, usually by incrementing or decremeting it. There is no reason to have a pull for every push—the stack may simply be adjusted by an increment in place of an actual transfer of data.

Interrupt action in regard to the stack varies according to the microprocessor. The 8080 does not automatically store any cpu register except for the program counter and flags by executing the RST instruction which is the vectored interrupt controller's response to the interrupt. Further saving of the cpu registers must be performed in the software interrupt processing routine. The 6502 is smiliar to the 8080 in that it saves only the contents of the program counter and processor flags when an interrupt occurs. The 6800 saves all cpu registers and status in response to an interrupt. In the return from an interrupt the same rule must be followed as in a return from a subroutine. The stack level must be restored to the same point as before the interrupt. Pushes performed by both the hardware interrupt action and software interrupt processing must be compensated for by pulls or pops or by proper adjustment of the stack pointer.

STACK OPERATIONS—8080

The stack pointer can be initialized by an LXI SP instruction which loads the stack pointer with the specified 16-bit intermediate value signifying top of stack+1. (The stack pointer is always decremented by one before storage of each byte).

```
TOPS    EQU     040000
        .
        .
        LXI     SP,TOPS
```

Calls to subroutines result in the link (contents of the program counter) being stored in the stack as follows:

STACK LOCATION N		PC most significant 8 bits
	N−1	PC least significant 8 bits

Pushes result in two bytes of data being transferred to the stack, either the two bytes of register pairs B,C, D,E, or H,L or the A register and cpu flags. The storage during a push is shown below:

STACK LOCATION N		Register pair ms 8 bits
	N−1	Register pair ls 8 bits
	or	
STACK LOCATION N		A register
	N−1	Flags

Since the interrupt response is the one-byte call, the RST instruction, the stack action is the same as for the CALL. In all of the above actions, the stack pointer after the stack action points to the last data byte transferred. It is always decremented by one before transferring the first byte of data on a CALL, PUSH, or RST.

The corresponding action taken on return, which is either a return from interrupt or a return from subroutine, is to reload the program counter from the two stack locations and to leave the stack pointer set to the location *above* the last data byte pulled, in preparation for a new push or pull. The POP instructions work similarly except that two bytes of data representing the register pairs or the A register and cpu flags are involved.

The stack pointer in the 8080 may be incremented or decremented by the INX SP and DCX SP instructions.

STACK OPERATIONS—6800

The stack pointer in the 6800 may be loaded by an LDS instruction. The load may be either an immediate value or a memory operand representing the top of stack. Here, unlike the 8080, the stack pointer is used as a pointer to the current top of stack for a push and then decremented.

```
        TOPS    EQU     $DFFF       TOP OF STACK
                .
                .
                LDS     #TOPS       INITIALIZE STACK P
```

A JSR instruction results in the following storage in the stack:

STACK LOCATION N		PC least significant 8 bits
	N−1	PC most significant 8 bits

Pushes transfer either the contents of the A accumulator or the contents of the B accumulator to the current stack location. Current status is stored in the stack during execution of the Software Interrupt instruction, SWI, during execution of the Wait for Interrupt instruction, WAI, or in response to either a NMI or external interrupt. The status is stored as follows:

STACK LOCATION N	PC least significant 8 bits
N−1	PC most significant 8 bits
N−2	Index reg ls 8 bits
N−3	Index reg ms 8 bits
N−4	Accumulator A
N−5	Accumulator B
N−6	Condition codes

The stack pointer is adjusted to point to the next available stack location.

Since the number of bytes pushed into the stack by a JSR differs from the number pushed for an interrupt, there are two separate returns, Return from Subroutine and Return from Interrupt, RTS and RTI, respectively. The RTS reloads the program counter only, while the RTI restores the data in reverse order from the manner in which it was pushed. PULA and PULB pull one byte of data from the stack, restoring either the A or B accumulator.

The stack pointer may be incremented or decremented by the INS or DES instructions. It may also be stored by the STX instruction, transferred to the index register by the TSX instruction, or loaded by the index register by the TXS instruction.

STACK OPERATIONS—6502

The stack pointer in the 6502 refers to the page 1 location of the stack. It can be loaded via the X index register by first loading the index register and then performing a TXS instruction to transfer the contents of the index register to the stack pointer. The stack pointer always points to the next available stack location, so the stack pointer must be initialized with the true top of stack.

```
TOPS    EQU     $FF         TOP OF STACK ($1FF)
        .
        .
        .
        LDX     #TOPS
        TXS                 INITIALIZE STACK POINTER
```

The JSR operates similarly to the 6800. The link (current contents of the program counter) is stored into the stack as follows:

STACK LOCATION N	PC most significant 8 bits
N−1	PC least significant 8 bits

Pushes push the contents of either the accumluator or the processor status register into the stack (PHA or PHP). Interrupt action in regard to the stack causes the contents of the program counter and flags (status register) to be pushed into the stack in the following manner:

STACK LOCATION N	PC most significant 8 bits
N−1	PC least significant 8 bits
N−2	Processor status register (flags)

The stack pointer is then adjusted to point to the next available stack location.

As in the 6800, there is a separate Return from Interrupt (RTI) and Return from Subroutine (RTS). Stack action results in data being pulled from the stack in reverse order from the way it was stored. Likewise, the PLA and PLP instructions pull either the accumulator or flags from the stack.

Unfortunately, there is no increment or decrement stack pointer instruction. The stack pointer can be modified by loading the index register with the stack pointer, incrementing or decrementing the index register the proper amount, and transferring the contents of the index register back to the stack pointer.

```
FOLLY   TSX     GET STACK POINTER
        INX
        INX     BYPASS LAST TWO ARGS
        TXS     RESTORE SP
        RTS     RETURN
```

Table Operations

Tables are sets of data in contiguous locations. Either by the displacement within the table or by other data associated with the table entry, a table may be used to correlate one piece of data with another. Each table is composed of data entries of a certain length. The total length of the table is the maximum number of data entries times the entry length. Within each entry, there may be subentries which may still be broken down further. Data is grouped within the table by a variety of means.

The displacement of the entry within the table may be used to look up the data item. An example of this would be a table of sine values that is 90 bytes long, with each entry within the table having a length of one byte. The coarse sine value of any angle from 0 to 90° could be found by adding the integer value of the angle to the start of the table and picking up the corresponding entry. The entry is assumed to be *scaled* by 256, that is, the value picked up would be the fractional sine value $\times$ 256, or an unsigned integer value from 00000000_2 through 11111111_2.

The opposite type of table from this first example is the type of table where the data item or the content of the table defines the displacement to be used in other operations. This might be used, for instance, in a system monitor routine. A system monitor would read user commands and perform a different function for each command. An ASCII "A" might cause the monitor to branch to the assembler, an "E" might cause the editor to be invoked, and a "D" night cause the debug program to be entered. In the actual implementation of the code to take a given character command, two tables might be used. The first table would consist of a table of all commands. If there were 13 one-byte commands, the table would be 13 bytes long, and each one-byte entry would consist of the character for that command. The second table would consist of 13 two-byte entries, each entry defining the corresponding address of the proper routine to be entered for the command. Note that there is a one-for-one correspondence between the two tables. The nth entry in TABL2 holds the address of the routine to be entered for the one-letter command given by the nth entry of TABL1. When a system command is input by the user the ASCII character is saved and a search is made of TABL1 for the character. If it is found, the displacement of the character from the start of TABL1 is multiplied by two to give a new index value. This index value is used to pick up the corresponding entry in TABL2, which is the transfer address for the system routine.

Another type of table is one in which the index is unimportant because a *key* is used to access information. Let's suppose that we have a directory of floppy disc files. Each entry in the directory table is fifteen bytes long. The first six bytes are the name of the file in ASCII. The next byte is the starting sector of the file on the disc. The eight and ninth bytes are the address in memory into which the file should be read. The tenth byte is a checksum of the file, the eleventh byte is a qualifier that defines the type of data in the file, and the four remaining bytes are spares. When a user requests the system monitor to READ a certain file from the floppy, a search will be made of the directory table for the given file name. The search will consist of a six-byte comparison at DISCD, DISCD+15, DISCD+30, and so forth, down through directory DISCD. If the file name is found, the additional parameters defining the file will be read and the disc file will be read into core accordingly. The index of the entry was unimportant in this case, except perhaps to define the end of the table.

Tables of the latter type may have data entries within the table ordered in different ways. Data entries may be completely unordered. The names of floppy disc files in the previous example might have been entered as they were created, generating a table of file names in no particular order. A second approach would be to arrange the file names in alphabetical order. As each new name was entered it would be *merged* into the table to preserve the alphabetical nature of the entries.

In a table of unordered entries, a *sequential search* must be made of the table to find the desired entry. The table is searched from beginning to end, with a comparison being made of each entry to the desired key. The average number of entries processed in this type of search is the number of table entries divided by two.

When a table is ordered in alphabetical or another type of ascending or descending order by entry, a sequential search can still be made, but there are several other types of searches that are much faster. One of these is the *binary search*. In the binary search the remaining area of the table to be searched is halved for each comparison. The half to be searched in the next comparison is determined by the relation of the current entry and the key. As an example of this type of search, take the following table, which has names in alphabetical order. The key is BACH. As each entry is picked, up, the current entry is compared with BACH. If BACH is greater in numeric value than the current entry the next half to be searched is located further down the table; if BACH is less, then the next half to be searched is further up the table. As each comparison is made, the remaining area to be searched is reduced by one-half. The first comparison is made

Entry 1	BACH	Fourth compare
2	BIZET	Third compare
3	DVORAK	Second compare
4	FRANCK	
5	LISZT	First compare
6	RAVEL	
7	ROSSINNI	
8	STRAUSS	
9	VERDI	

half-way through the table. Each new comparison is made at the half-way entry of the remaining area. The worst-case number of comparisons that must be made to find any entry is given by

$$N = \log_2 (\text{total number of entries})_{RU} + 1$$

where RU stands for "rounded up." In this example $\log_2(9)_{RU} = 4$, as $\log_2 (9) = 4.XX$. Another way of describing the formula is the following: Take the total number of entries and find the largest power of two that will divide into the total number. If the division is even, add one; if the division is not even, add two. The $+1$ portion of the formula modifies the binary search for the case where the key is not found. If the next entry to be searched is the same as the last, the search is done and the key is not in the table.

A third type of search is based on a *hash*. A hash is nothing more than some arbitrary formula to find a key to look up an entry in a table of hashes. The hash value may be unique or not unique. One way to implement the symbol-table search of an assembler program would be to perform a binary search on each string of ASCII characters representing a symbol. Even a binary search takes time, however, when a long string of data must be compared. If the number of bytes to be compared could be reduced, than the search might be significantly speeded up. By allowing only alphabetic, numeric, and a few special characters in a symbol name a number can be derived for each character that can be represented by 0 through 39_{10} as shown in the list in the following page.

ASCII	Base 40	ASCII	Base 40	ASCII	Base 40
°	0	B	14	P	28
/	1	C	15	Q	29
0	2	D	16	R	30
1	3	E	17	S	31
2	4	F	18	T	32
3	5	G	19	U	33
4	6	H	20	V	34
5	7	I	21	W	35
6	8	J	22	X	36
7	9	K	23	Y	37
8	10	L	24	Z	38
9	11	M	25	blank	39
@	12	N	26		
A	13	O	27		

Now it happens that three base-40 digits fit nicely in 16 bits as $40^3 = 64,000 < 2^{16} = 65,536$ and that a six-character symbolic name could be hashed into four bytes ($4 \times 8 = 32$ bits), a hash which is in this case a unique hash. The binary search could now be done using a four-byte key instead of six bytes with consequent savings in comparison times.

Hashes that result in values that are not unique may also be used to advantage. A hash of a five-character symbol could produce a single-byte value. Although the value might not be unique (the symbols VALUE and VALUU might produce the same hash value, for example) the chances are very good that most of the hashes produced in a typical assembly would be unique. Any values that had more than one symbol associated with it could point to a short list of all the symbols associated with that hash value and the overall searching process would still be very efficient.

Another type of data structure is an array. A table is a one-dimensional array when the entry in the table is referenced by the displacement from the beginning of the table, or the index. Data can be arranged in two-dimensional arrays or even in n-dimensional arrays. A two-dimensional array can be thought of as a checkerboard matrix where a data element is indexed by row number and column number. A three-dimensional array can be visualized as a three-dimensional tic-tac-toe arrangement where the data elements are indexed by x, y, and z coordinates. Arrays of n dimensions are harder to visualize, but find a great deal of use in mathematically oriented programming. The techniques for accessing two-dimensional arrays will be demonstrated in this chapter. These techniques can be expanded by the reader to cover multidimensional accesses.

TABLE OPERATIONS—8080

The 8080 is oriented toward table entries that are multiples of 8 bits in length, as are all the microprocessors discussed here. It is convenient to index through a table in a sequential search by using the B,C, D,E, or H,L register pairs as index registers as in the following example, where the key is contained in the B register.

```
SRCHT   LDA    KEY         LOAD KEY FOR SEARCH
        MOV    B,A         SETUP B WITH KEY
        MVI    C,TABL      SETUP TABLE LENGTH+1
        LXI    D,TABI      GET TABLE START
LOOP    DCR    C           DECREMENT INDEX
        JZ     NFND        GO IF NOT FOUND
        LDAX   D           GET NEXT ENTRY
        CMP    B           COMPARE ENTRY TO KEY
        JZ     FND         GO IF FND
        INX    D           BUMP POINTER*
        JMP    LOOP
         .
         .
TAB1    DS     . .
TABL    EQU    $−TAB1+1    LENGTH+1
```

The instruction at * bumps the pointer by one byte. For an *n*-byte entry the pointer could be adjusted for *n* bytes. This routine is generalized to work with any length of table including one of zero length.

Comparisons of more than one byte are more tedious. The following routine compares a two-byte key with a two-byte entry. The size of each entry is three bytes with the third byte possibly containing additional data about the entry. Two comparisons are made and if there is no match the index registers are incremented past the third byte of the entry in preparation for the next entry.

```
SRCHT   MVI    B,TABL      TABLE LENGTH+3
        LHLD   KEY         KEY TO H,L
        LXI    D,TAB1      START OF TABLE
LOOP    MOV    A,B
        SUI    A,3
        MOV    B,A         INDEX−3
        JZ     NFND        GO IF NOT FOUND
        LDAX   D           GET FIRST BYTE
        CMP    H           COMPARE 1ST BYTE
        INX    D           POINT TO NEXT BYTE
        JNZ    NEXT        GO IF NO MATCH
        LDAX   D           GET SECOND BYTE
        CMP    L           COMPARE 2ND BYTE
        JZ     FND         GO IF MATCH
NEXT    INX    D           BYPASS NEXT BYTE
```

```
        JMP   LOOP          TRY AGAIN
        .
        .
TAB1    DS    . .
TABL    EQU   $-TAB1+3      LENGTH + 3
```

Another method that might be used to terminate a comparison through a table is to put a unique value at the end of the table. If the table is made up of ASCII data, for example, the terminating entry in the table might be -1, which is not a valid ASCII character. This allows for tables of variable length and simplifies the checks for the table end. The search in the first example would be shortened to:

```
SRCHT   LDA   KEY           LOAD KEY FOR SEARCH
        MOV   B,A           SETUP B WITH KEY
        LXI   D,TAB1        GET TABLE START
LOOP    LDAX  D             GET NEXT ENTRY
        CPI   -1
        JZ    NFND          GO IF NOT FOUND
        CMP   B             COMPARE ENTRY TO KEY
        JZ    FND           GO IF FOUND
        INX   D             BUMP POINTER
        JMP   LOOP
```

The general method for picking up data from arrays depends upon the arrangement of the array in memory. If the array has n columns and m rows then the total number of elements is $n \times m$. The array can be arranged in memory in the order C_0,R_0, C_0,R_1, C_0,R_2, . . . , C_0,R_{m-1}, C_1,R_0, . . . or can be arranged R_0,C_0, R_0,C_1, . . . , R_0,C_{n-1}, R_1,C_0, . . . In the first case the displacement from the start of the array storage area is given by $(C \times m) + R$, where C is the column number (beginning with 0), m is the number of rows, and R is the row number (beginning with 0). The second case displacement is determined by $(R \times n) + C$, where n is the number of columns. This same access arrangement can be expanded into multidimensional arrays. A two-dimensional access example follows. Here the row of the array is in CURRW and the column of the array is in CURCL and the array elements are one byte in length, arranged in C_0,R_0 fashion. The number of rows in the array is variable and is given in NOROW. Use is made

```
GETAR   LDA   CURCL         GET COL #
        MOV   B,A           MULTIPLICAND
        LDA   NOROW         # OF ROWS
        CALL  MULT          C X M IN A
        MOV   B,A
        LDA   CURRW         GET RW #
        ADD   B             C X M + R
        LXI   D,O
        MOV   E,A           MOVE DISPLACEMENT
```

```
        LXI    H,ARRAY      START OF ARRAY
        DAD    D            START + DISP
        MOV    M            GET ELEMENT
```

of a single-precision multiply called MULT which returns the product in A.

TABLE OPERATIONS—6800

A sequential search through a table terminated by a −1 is shown below. Each entry is five bytes long with the search being made on a one-byte key which is the first byte of every entry. Incrementing the

```
SRCHT   LDAA   KEY          PICKUP KEY
        LDX    #TAB1        START OF TABLE
        LDAB   #−1          TERMINATION
LOOP    CMPB   X            CHECK TERMINATE
        BEQ    NFND         GO IF NOT FOUND
        CMPA   X            CHECK BYTE
        BEQ    FND          GO IF FOUND
        INX
        INX
        INX
        INX
        INX                 POINT TO NEXT ENTRY
        JMP    LOOP
```

index register more than a byte or two at a time is a problem not only on the 6800, but on the other two microprocessors as well. Perhaps a subroutine could have been used for a double-precision increment of *n,* but the speed and storage of five INXs is probably most efficient.

The equivalent array access for the same type of two-dimensional array as discussed for the 8080 is shown below. Here the array is

```
GETAR   LDAB   CURCL        GET COL #
        LDAA   NOROW        MULTIPLIER
        JSR    MULT         C X M IN A
        ADDA   CURRW        C X M + R
        STAA   INXR+1
        CLR    INXR         DISP IN INXR, INXR+
        LDX    INXR         SETUP DISP
        LDAA   ARRAY,X      GET ELEMENT
```

small enough to be in page 0. If the array had been somewhere else in memory then the LDAA ARRAY,X would not have worked, since ARRAY could not have been resolved in the one-byte displacement of the instruction. In that case, the following code might have been used at the expense of reentrancy. Here the displacement in the LDAA

```
GETAR   LDAB    CURCL       GET COL #
        LDAA    NOROW       MULTIPLIER
        JSR     MULT        C X M IN A
        ADDA    CURRW       C X M + R
        STAA    DISP        MODIFY INSTRUCTION
        LDX     #ARRAY      START OF ARRAY
        LDAA    O,X         THIS INSTRUCTION MODIFIED
DISP    EQU     *-1
```

instruction is dynamically modified with the displacement of the array element from the start of the array. The index register is then loaded with the address of the start of the array, and the array element can be picked up with the modified LDAA.

TABLE OPERATIONS—6502

Sequential searching through a table terminated by a −1 is somewhat similar to the 6800 in the 6502 except that it is easier to modify the index registers as they are only single-precision values.

```
SRCHT   LDX     #0          INITIALIZE INDEX
LOOP    LDA     TAB1,X      GET TABLE ENTRY
        CMP     MNUS1       COMPARE TO −1
        BEQ     NFND        GO IF NOT FOUND
        CMP     KEY         COMPARE TO KEY
        BEQ     FND         GO IF FOUND
        TXA                 INDEX TO A
        CLC                 CLEAR C
        ADC     #5          ADD 5
        TAX                 NOW HAVE INDEX + 5
        JMP     LOOP        GO FOR NEXT ENTRY
```

Many times it is convenient to index through several tables with the same index value applied to each table. In a system that can run five user's programs simultaneously (actually concurrently) in memory at the same time, information about the user's programs might be contained in a set of tables indexed by a user number, 0 through 5. USATB might be a table containing the starting address of the user's program, UTOPT might contain the type of program, and UEOPT might contain the address of the end of the user's program. Here's an example of how the user number in one of the index registers could be used to pick up information if the X index always had the current user number through the monitor program code.

```
        LDX     USRNO       GET USER #
        CPX     #−1
        BEQ     NOUSR       GO IF NO USER
        .
        .
```

```
        LDA   USATB,X      GET USER'S START
        .
        .
        LDA   UTOPT,X      GET USER'S TYPE
        .
        LDA   UEOPT,X      GET USER'S END LOCATION
        .
        .
USRNO   FCB   −1
USATB   RMB   5            HOLDS USER START
UTOPT   RMB   5            HOLDS USER TYPE
UEOPT   RMB   5            HOLDS USER END LOC
```

Equivalent code for an access of a two-dimensional array follows.

```
GETAR   LDX   CURCL        GET COL #
        LDA   NOROW        MULTIPLIER
        JSR   MULT         C X M IN A
        CLC
        ADC   CURRW        C X M + R
        TAX                NOW HAVE INDEX
        LDA   ARRAY,X      GET ELEMENT
```

Here the code is very short and sweet as the displacement field of the
LDA instruction can be resolved in two bytes.

FURTHER EXAMPLES

Further examples of table operations are given in the programming
algorithms part (Chap. 25) of this book.

List Processing

Although tables and arrays are subsets of list data structures when discussed formally, the lists discussed here will refer to a special type of data structure. An analogy to a computerized list would be a game to find hidden objects. The player is given a slip of paper upon which is written the start of the hunt. The player then finds the starting place, picks up the object, and finds another piece of paper with directions to the next hiding place. The search then continues with each place that an object is stored yielding new directions. Finally, the last object, the grand prize, is found and the game ends.

The computerized list is similar to the game. A variable in memory points to the *head* of the list, or the first item in the list. Each entry in the list is made up of the data item itself and a pointer to the next data item in the list. In this way the items in the list are chained in forward fashion, each item always having a pointer that defines the location of the next item. The last item in the list is defined by a variable in memory that points to the *tail* of the list, or last item. The items in the list do not have to occupy contiguous memory locations and may be spread throughout memory in any fashion. A representative *single-ended* list such as we have been describing is shown on the following page. Each pointer is 16 bits long and the data item in the list is one byte long.

In this case either TAIL or the next address pointer could define the last item in the list. The next address value of 177777_8 would be a flag indicating that this entry was the last entry in the list.

A *double-ended* list would not point forward to the next data item, but would point backwards to the last data item. In the above example there would be not only a two-byte forward address, but a

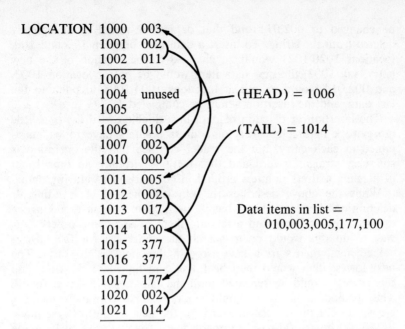

two-byte backward address. A value of all ones would denote the end of the list in either direction, and HEAD and TAIL would still point to the beginning and end items in the list.

As the reader can see, a great deal more storage is taken up by listing data in this fashion rather than by constructing a tabular list of consecutive values. The great advantage of a list, however, is the ability to easily merge, delete, and modify new data items. In a table of increasing values a new value can be inserted by moving all the values below the insertion point downwards. Similarly, deleting a value leaves a gap that must be filled with data below by moving it up in a block. For long tables, this block movement of data becomes very expensive in terms of processing time. If a table is 200 bytes long, the average entry or deletion would necessitate moving 100 bytes of data, perhaps 25 microseconds for each byte of data moved or 2.5 milliseconds for every insertion or deletion. In addition to the time spent in moving the data, there is a search time to find the entry or deletion point of perhaps 3 milliseconds as each entry is picked up, compared to the key, the index is incremented and compared to the last table value, and so forth. In a list the search time would be about the same, or could even be shortened by having intermediate pointers that point to locations part way down the list. The block movement time, however, would be made almost nothing by changing the address links in the list. To delete data item 3 in the above list, for example, the address pointer at locations 1007,1010 would be changed to 002,011 and that data item would be completely deleted from the string. To insert a data item between 177 and 100, locations 1020,1021 would be changed to the location of the new entry, say 1003, the new data item would be put at location 1003, and 002,014 would be put at locations 1004,1005 to point to the last data, and the insertion would be completed.

The insertion or deletion of data in a double-ended list is a little more work in that two sets of address pointers have to be maintained in each entry, but the reader can see that the operation is still very straightforward and that there is virutally no time spent in juggling address pointers around in comparison to moving data.

While the above describes the physical method of inserting or deleting one item in a list, what is the implementation of taking an unsorted list of items and arranging them in ascending order? One way to do this would be to search the entire list for the lowest-valued item, then start a new list with that item at the head. The next lowest item would then be found and linked to the first, and the process would be repeated until the tail of the list was found. This method, although it would work, requires two large memory areas, one for the old list and one for the new. If the list was made up of 100 items 100 passes through the list would have to be made with about 5000 comparisons being made, as the first search would involve 100 items, the next 99, the next 98, and so forth.

An alternative method of ordering the list is called a *bubble sort*. It uses much less memory than the other type of sort. In the bubble sort, passes through the list are made as before, but each data item is compared to the previous data item and swapped with that data item if it is of lower value. In this manner, the lower-valued data items (lighter?) bubble to the top of the list. The sort is complete when no swaps are made. Let's see how this works, remembering that if the next data item is lower-valued it is swapped with the previous one, and if it is higher-valued no swap is made. The links in the list are left out for clarity. Individual items would be swapped by changing address pointers just as was done in the insert and delete examples. See p. 143.

In this example it took six passes plus one final pass to determine that there were no further swaps to be made to sort the entire list. The actual number of comparisons is slightly more than the first type of search, but no additional memory for the new list was required. This can be very beneficial in any size system, since the larger the memory area for the sort, the less overhead there is in bringing in new data from the secondary storage device, and the more efficient the sort.

Sorts are used very frequently in business-oriented processing and information retrieval systems. If the reader's microcomputer system

Bubble Sort

Before	After Pass 1	After Pass 2	After Pass 3
1	1	1	1
17	17	2	2
101	2	5	5
2	5	17	17
5	45	37	16
45	37	16	3
37	16	3	37
16	3	45	45
3	101	101	101

After Pass 4	After Pass 5	After Pass 6
1	1	1
2	2	2
5	5	3
16	3	5
3	16	16
17	17	17
37	37	37
45	45	45
101	101	101

will be used to produce mailing lists, to catalog documents, or to order any data that is entered into the system in unordered or on an as required basis, than the efficiency and speed of the sort program will become very important.

Another related operation to the sort is the operation of *merging* data. Here the data is in ordered form, but in two separate lists. Let's somewhat arbitrarily call one the *master* list and one the *update* list. The entries in the *update* list are to be merged into the entries in the master list to produce a new master list that has ordered entries. Here the method of merging the data is to pick up the first entry in the update list and then search the master list until the insertion point is found. The current update entry is then inserted, the pointers changed, and the next update entry is then used to search the master list. When the last update entry has been inserted, the new master list is completed. Although the bubble sort method could be used to add the new entries to the master list, this would be a rather inefficient way of solving the problem when the two lists are already ordered.

As can be surmised from the above, some processing of data might involve several subtasks of ordering one list, ordering another, merging the two lists, and so forth.

LIST PROCESSING—8080

The following 8080 example searches a single-ended list for a value held in the A register. HEAD points to the head of the list and the tail of the list is defined by all ones in the address link. The data and address link are arranged as shown below.

```
ENTRY  +0   8-bit data value
       +1   8-lsb of address link
       +2   8-msb of address link

        LHLD   HEAD     LOAD HEAD ADDRESS
LOOP    LDA    VALUE    SEARCH VALUE
        CMP    M        COMPARE WITH ENTRY
        BEQ    FND      GO IF FOUND
        INX    H        POINT TO LSB OF LINK
        XCHG            H,L TO D,E
        LDAX   D        LOAD LSB OF LINK
        MOV    L,A      MOVE TO L
        INX    D        POINT TO MSB OF LINK
        LDAX   D        LOAD MSB OF LINK
        MOV    H,A      MOVE TO H
        CPI    −1       COMPARE FOR TAIL
        JNZ    LOOP     GO IF NOT TAIL
NFND    .                NOT FOUND
        .
```

The not found portion of code is executed when a −1 is found in the most significant byte of the link address. If the link is not 377/XXX and the current value is not the search value, then the link address is moved into the H,L register pair in preparation for picking up the next entry.

LIST PROCESSING—6800

The code for a search of the same type of list as above for the 6800 follows. Here the code is facilitated because the index register can be loaded by an indexed type of addressing. This means that if the index register points to the link address, that link may be easily loaded into the index register by performing an LDX X.

```
        LDX    HEAD     LOAD HEAD ADDRESS
        LDAA   VALUE    SEARCH VALUE
LOOP    CMPA   X        COMPARE CURRENT WITH VALUE
        BEQ    FND      GO IF FOUND
```

```
        INX                POINT TO LINK ADDRESS
        LDX    X           LOAD NEW LINK
        CPX    #−1         COMPARE TO TAIL VALUE
        BNE    LOOP        GO IF NOT END OF LIST
NFND    .                  NOT FOUND
```

A bubble sort may also be performed on a table of data, especially if a list is not necessary for merging new data. The following example assumes a table of 8-bit data values. The data is to be sorted by a bubble sort. A memory flag word, SWAP, is zero until the first two bytes of data are swapped in the sorting process. If on any pass down through the table no swap is necessary, SWAP is never set and the sort is terminated. There are two nested loops in the routine. The first, from LOOP to NEXT−1, checks every table entry and swaps the current entry with the last if necessary. On the last entry of the table, the index value equals TABE and the second loop is entered, which tests SWAP at NEXT and loops back to LOP1 if at least one SWAP was done during the first pass through the table. LOP1 clears SWAP and sets up the index to the beginning of the table for the next sort.

```
LOP1    CLR    SWAP        CLEAR SWAP FLAG
        LDX    #TAB1−1     INITIALIZE INDEX
LOOP    INX                BUMP INDEX
        CPX    #TABE       AT END OF TABLE?
        BEQ    NEXT        GO IF YES
        LDAA   0,X         LOAD TABLE ENTRY
        LDAB   1,X         LOAD NEXT ENTRY
        CBA                COMPARE TWO ENTRIES
        BLE    LOOP        GO IF ORDER OK
        INC    SWAP        SET SWAP FLAG
        STAA   1,X         SWAP
        STAB   0,X
        JMP    LOOP        GO FOR NEXT
NEXT    TST    SWAP        TEST FOR SWAP
        BNE    LOP1        GO IF NOT DONE
DONE    .                  SORTED
        .
        .
TAB1    RMB    . . .       TABLE
TABE    EQU    *           LAST LOCATION IN TABLE+1
```

LIST PROCESSING—6502

The code for a search of the same type as above is shown below for the 6502. Here some modifications of a page 0 pointer are necessary to enable addressing of the 16-bit link. These addresses, of course, are not known beforehand, and this is one of several approaches to dynamically changing the effective address as new link addresses are found. The pointer in page 0 holds the least significant 8 bits of the link address in DEST and the most significant 8 bits in DEST+1. The 16 bits of DEST are used in conjunction with the Y register in an indirect indexed addressing mode of operation. The reader will recall that in this mode a page 0 indirect address is picked up and the contents of the Y index register are added to it to form the new effective address. By using DEST to hold the address of each new entry in the list, the three bytes of the entry may be picked up by indices of 0, 1, and 2 in the Y register.

```
        LDA   HEAD        MSB OF HEAD ADDRESS
        STA   DEST+1
        LDA   HEAD+1      LSB OF HEAD ADDRESS
        STA   DEST
LOOP    LDY   #0          INDEX TO VALUE
        LDA   VALUE       SEARCH VALUE
        CMP   (DEST),Y    COMPARE WITH ENTRY
        BEQ   FND         GO IF FOUND
        INY               INDEX TO LSB OF LINK
        LDA   (DEST),Y    GET LSB
        PHA               SAVE
        INY               INDEX TO MSB OF LINK
        LDA   (DEST),Y    GET MSB
        CMP   #−1         TEST FOR TAIL
        BEQ   NFND        GO IF NOT FND
        STA   DEST+1      INITIALIZE MSB
        PLA               GET LSB OF LINK
        STA   DEST        INITIALIZE LSB
        JMP   LOOP        CONTINUE
NFND    .                 NOT FOUND
        .
```

Bit Processing and Manipulation

Bit processing and manipulation is necessary in microcomputers and in all computers because not everything can be arranged in 8-bit fields in a program or hardware device. We've already seen the need for 5-bit codes in Baudot representation, program flags with the least significant bit or most significant bit or both set, and instruction fields that represent register addresses. Suffice it to say that at one time or another a programmer will have to deal with the problem of retrieving data from a field within 8 bits, testing the field, or merging the field into the 8-bit byte.

Retrieving a one- to seven-bit field from an 8-bit byte is typically handled by *masking* out the field and shifting it right until the field is aligned so that its least significant bit is in bit position 0. The contents of the accumulator or memory location then hold the true value of the field. Suppose that an 8080 instruction set is to be *simulated* on a 6800 microcomputer. An 8080 program will be loaded into the 6800 microcomputer and the 6800 will interpret the 8080 instructions by analyzing each instruction and then simulating the 8080 registers and flags in software pseudo-registers and flags. If an LXI RP instruction is detected, the 6800 program will simulate the 8080 instruction by loading the specified register pair, represented by two memory locations, with the intermediate data from bytes 2 and 3 of the instruction. To do this, the RP field of the first byte of the 8080 instruction must be analyzed to determine which pseudo-register pair must be loaded. The implementation of this is as follows:

1. The first byte of the instruction is ANDed with 00110000_2. This masks out all bits but the RP field.

instruction byte	00RP0001
AND value	00110000
AND result	00RP0000

2. The RP field is now shifted right four bits to align it (right justify it) with the lsb.

AND result	00RP0000
shift 4 bits	000000RP

3. The result may now be tested for the value of 00, 01, 10, or 11_2 representing register pairs B,C, D,E, H,L, or SP, respectively.

Note that in this case the shift was a logical right shift or rotate. Although an arithmetic shift would have worked, it's best to get into the habit of *not* using one in this alignment operation lest the reader forget when the sign bit happens to be in the affected field. The second step is optional if the field could be used without alignment. Many times the alignment makes further use of the field less confusing and more convenient, however.

Storing a one- to seven-bit field in a byte involves ANDing the affected byte to reset the field to all zeros, and then merging the new value of the field into the byte by an inclusive OR operation. Suppose that the 6800 is being used to assemble an 8080 program. (There's no reason that a *cross-assembler* such as this would not be just as efficient as an 8080 microcomputer assembling 8080 program code.) In constructing the 8080 MOV R,M instruction, the 6800 has produced the following code for the one-byte instruction: $01XXX110_2$. The Xs represent indeterminate bits, or in programming language, garbage. Having read the argument from the assembler source line the 6800 program discovers that register E is to be used to make the instruction MOV E,M. It then takes the 011_2 value that will represent the E code and stores it in the XXX field as shown in the following steps:

1. The instruction skeleton is ANDed with 11000111_2 to reset the XXX to zero.

skeleton	01XXX110
AND value	11000111
AND result	01000110

2. The 011 value is shifted three bits to the left to align it in the proper field position.

code	00000011
aligned	00011000

3. The aligned value is now merged into the skeleton by an OR.

skeleton	01000110
aligned	
code	00011000
OR result	01011110

The ANDing operation initially is not necessary if the programmer is certain that the field is already zero.

Testing a field within a byte has several alternatives. If only a one-bit field is to be tested, then an AND can be performed and the zero flag tested for zero or nonzero (zero or one in the field). If more than one bit is to be tested the field may be retrieved by the method above of ANDing and shifting the result to align the field at the right end of the register. Another alternative that avoids the shifting operation would be to AND out the field, and then test the result by a number scaled up by the appropriate amount. As an example of the last method, suppose that we would like to ascertain whether a three-bit field in bits 6–4 of the byte holds a value greater than 100_2. In other words, is the byte $X101XXXX$, $X110XXXX$, or $X111XXXX_2$, where the Xs are bits other than the field? The operation would be performed as follows:

1. AND the byte containing the field with 01110000.

byte	XFFFXXXX
AND	01110000
result	0FFF0000

2. The result of the AND is $FFF_2 \times 16$, so a comparison can be made with 01010000_2.

   Compare 0FFF0000 with 01010000.

3. If the result is positive then the field must contain 101, 110, or 111.

01010000	01100000	01110000
−01010000	−01010000	−01010000
00000000	00010000	00100000

The above operations have all treated fields as one to seven bits within a basic byte. Fields of this size will occur in a large number of applications. Fields larger than 8 bits are, of course, possible. A field may be any number of bits. When larger fields are necessary, it is convenient to make the fields multiples of 8 bits to take advantage of the efficiency of working with bytes in the microcomputer. This is also true for groups of fields, such as table entries. Suppose that we have specified a set of characters which are to be output to a vdm. The set of characters is held in a table. Each entry of the table holds the x coordinate, or character position along the line, the y coordinate, or line number, and the character itself. Now x can be 0–31_{10}, y can be 0–15_{10}, and the character is a seven-bit character. What is the best way to store the data in a table?

The x coordinate can be held in 5 bits, the y in 4 bits, and the character in 7 bits, for a total of 16 bits. One possible arrangement would be as follows:

Byte 0	XXXXXYYY	X, 3 bits of Y
Byte 1	YCCCCCCC	1 bit of Y, 7 bits of character

This arrangement, however, would require quite a bit of manipulation to get the YYYY value; data from two bytes would have to be merged. On the other hand the data is *packed* quite nicely and the efficiency in terms of memory storage is optimized. The easiest and fastest access method would be to store the data in three bytes:

Byte 0	000XXXXX	X
Byte 1	0000YYYY	Y
Byte 2	0CCCCCCC	character

In this case the data takes up 50 percent more storage, but as long as the number of points is small, this is not an important factor. Either way will work, with one being more efficient in storage, and the other more efficient in terms of processing time.

BIT PROCESSING—8080

The general method for retrieving a field from within a byte is shown in the following example. This code retrieves a field of 3 bits from within the following byte, $XXFFFXXX_2$, where X is other than the field and FFF is the field itself. The field is right justified in the A register at the end of the routine.

```
GETFD   LDA   WORD    WORD HOLDS FIELD
        RRC
        RRC
        RRC           ALIGN FFF
        ANI   07      MASK OUT FFF
        .
        .
```

Note that here it was convenient to shift and align the field first to avoid having to reset the carry on the first RRC instruction. Storing a field is identical with the previously discussed method. Here the same field is stored.

```
STOFD   LDA   WORD    WORD TO HOLD FIELD
        ANI   0307    MASK OUT FIELD
        MOV   B,A     HOLD SKELETON
```

```
LDA   FIELD    GET FIELD IN FORM FFF
RLC
RLC            ALIGN FIELD — ZEROES
RLC              TO VACATED BITS
ORA   B        MERGE FIELD INTO WORD
 .
 .
```

Testing a one-bit field within a byte can be easily done by ANDing the byte with an immediate value that defines the bit to be tested and jumping on a JZ or JNZ (0 or 1).

```
TESTB  LDA   WORD    CONTAINS FIELD
       ANI   MASK    MASK HAS 1 IN TEST BIT POS
       JZ    ZERO    GO IF BIT=0
ONE    .             BIT=1
       .
```

Whenever possible code should be *parameterized* to be usable in the general case, so that the wheel is patented only once. An example of this is in the following code, which gets the nth bit (7 through 0) out of the mth word of a table. One possible use for this would be in finding the value of the dot in a given matrix that is being displayed on a video display, the dot being either off or on. Another routine first converts the x,y coordinate of the dot to a displacement m from the start of the buffer and the position of the dot within the word n. Elements m and n are in locations EM and EN, respectively.

```
READB  LXI   H,BUF   GET START OF BUFFER
       XCHG          SAVE IN D,E
       LDA   EM      M
       MOV   L,A     SETUP H,L FOR ADD
       MVI   H,0
       DAD   D       FIND START OF BUFFER+M
       LDA   EN
       MOV   C,A     INITIALIZE CNT(N)
       MOV   A,M     GET WORD
LOP    DCR   C       DECREMENT INDEX
       JM    FND     GO IF DONE SHIFTING
       RRC           ROTATE BIT RIGHT
       JMP   LOP
FND    ANI   1       FIND BIT, 0 OR 1
       RET
```

A similar type of routine could be used to store a bit in bit position n in word m of a table, or the routine could even be expanded to parameterize the number of bits in the field, the length of table entries, and so forth.

BIT PROCESSING—6800

The method of retrieving a variable-length field within a memory byte is identical with the 8080 approach.

```
GETFD   LDAA   WORD      WORD HOLDS FIELD
        RORA
        RORA
        RORA             ALIGN FIELD
        ANDA   #7        MASK OUT FFF
         .
```

Similarly, the storage of an *n*-bit field is handled by the following:

```
STOFD   LDAA   WORD      WORD TO HOLD FIELD
        ANDA   #$C7      MASK OUT FIELD
        ASL    FIELD
        ASL    FIELD
        ASL    FIELD     ALIGN FIELD
        ORAA   FIELD     MERGE FIELD INTO WORD
         .
         .
```

Here the shifting of the field could be accomplished by shifting the memory location containing the field, although the field could have been put into the B accumulator for shifting.

Testing a one-bit field inside a byte is also identical with the 8080 approach.

```
TEST    LDAA   WORD      CONTAINS BIT TO BE TESTED
        ANDA   #MASK     MASK HAS 1 IN BIT POSTN
        BEQ    ZERO      GO IF ZERO
ONE      .               BIT=1
         .
```

Testing the sign bit may be done with the TST instruction mentioned previously which sets the zero or minus flag.

```
TEST    TST    WORD      TEST BIT 7
        BMI    ONE       GO IF SET
ZERO     .               BIT=0
         .
```

Sometimes it is necessary or convenient to test bits through the carry or sign bit position. An example of this would be the following routine, which tests the 8 bits in a byte by rotating left into the carry, and stores either a one or zero dependent upon the bit into memory locations BUF through BUF+7. A later routine changes these buffer locations into ASCII ones and zeros by inclusive ORing the hexadecimal value 30 with each of the eight locations. The binary contents of the location can then be printed out.

```
STRIP   LDAA   PRINT      BYTE TO BE PRINTED
        LDX    BUF        BUFFER START ADDRESS
        LDAB   #8         INDEX
LOOP    DECB              DECREMENT INDEX
        BMI    DONE       GO IF DONE
        CLR    X          CLEAR BUFFER BYTE
        ASLA              SHIFT OUT BIT
        BCC    NEXT       BRANCH IF 0
        INC    X          SET BUFFER BYTE TO 1
NEXT    INX               POINT TO NEXT BYTE
        BRA    LOOP       GO FOR NEXT
DONE    .
        .
```

BIT PROCESSING—6502

The methods of retrieving and storing fields within a memory byte are similar to the 8080 and 6800 approaches.

```
GETFD   LDA    WORD       WORD HOLDS FIELD
        LSR    A
        LSR    A
        LSR    A          ALIGN FIELD
        AND    #7         MASK OUT FFF
        .
        .

STOFD   LDA    WORD       WORD TO HOLD FIELD
        AND    #$C7       MASK OUT FIELD
        ASL    FIELD
        ASL    FIELD
        ASL    FIELD      ALIGN FIELD
        ORA    FIELD      MERGE FIELD INTO WORD
        .
        .
```

The 6502 has no TST as in the 6800, but a test of any bit within a memory byte may be made by the BIT instruction.

```
TEST    LDA    #MASK      MASK HAS ONE IN TEST BIT
        BIT    WORD       CONTAINS BIT TO BE TESTED
        BEQ    ZERO       GO IF ZERO
ONE     .                 BIT=1
        .
```

For a further example of bit manipulation, let's take the same buffer as in the previous example, only this time we'll be inputing ASCII ones and zeros and changing them into 8 bits which are stored in a byte in memory called BYTE. Assume that the eight ASCII bytes are in BUF through BUF+7, that all have been checked and found to be valid ASCII ones or zeros (hexadecimal 30 and 31), and that the first byte represents the msb of the byte to be assembled.

```
ASSEM   LDX   #0        CLEAR INDEX
        LDA   #0
        STA   BYTE      CLEAR RESULT
LOOP    SEC             1 TO CARRY FOR SUBTRACT
        LDA   BUF,X     LOAD ASCII BYTE
        SBC   #$30      CONVERT TO ZERO OR ONE
        CLC             0 TO CARRY FOR SHIFT
        BEQ   NEXT      GO IF NOT ONE
        SEC             THIS IS ONE, SET C
NEXT    ROL   BYTE      SHIFT 0 OR 1 AND PARTIAL
        INX             BUMP INDEX
        CPX   #8        COMPARE TO LAST INDEX+1
        BNE   LOOP      NOT DONE
DONE    .
```

Here the decoded bits from the ASCII buffer are first converted to a binary 0 or 1, and then shifted into location BYTE by a rotate left shift. Eight shifts are required.

Decimal and Floating-Point Arithmetic

This chapter discusses two common ways of handling data in microcomputers. The first, decimal arithmetic, is treated because all of the microprocessors discussed here have a decimal arithmetic capability in their instruction set. The second, floating-point representation, is not implemented in the hardware, but is extremely important when a large range of numbers is to be represented in microcomputers.

Decimal arithmetic was treated in earlier chapters in regard to how the microcomputer accomplishes a decimal add or subtract. The "half-carry" of the arithmetic and logical unit is used primarily for the decimal arithmetic function. The half-carry is called the AC (auxiliary carry) in the 8080 and the H flag (half-carry) in the 6800. The 6502 has no corresponding flag. Decimal arithmetic is performed in the 8080 and 6800 by executing a Decimal Adjust instruction after an add or subtract. The microprocessor logic then properly adjusts the sum or difference to a decimal, or bcd, result. In the 6502 a decimal flag (D) is set prior to the decimal operation. The following add or subtract is then performed in decimal fashion. Operands taking part in the decimal add or subtract must be bcd operands as discussed in Chapter 5.

A decimal operand has the format of $HHHHLLLL_2$, where HHHH is the high-order bcd digit and LLLL is the low-order bcd digit. Valid bcd digits are 0000_2 through 1001_2, representing the bcd values 0 through 9. Each byte can therefore hold a bcd value of 00_{10} through 99_{10}. Binary values such as 10111111_2 are meaningless in bcd format and will yield invalid results if used. This is an extension of the programmer's basic axiom, "garbage in—garbage out" (gigo).

Since a range of 0 through 99_{10} is not very usable, decimal representation can involve long strings of bcd data, which can be added or subtracted in multiple-precision just as binary data can. The carry of the most significant bit is used to implement the carry to higher-order bcd digits. In addition some limited multiplication and division can be performed in software packages or hardware plug-in modules that use bcd format.

Why use bcd or decimal arithmetic? For one thing, it is extremely easy to convert from ASCII to bcd format and back again. All that is involved to convert to bcd form is to take two ASCII digits representing 0 through 9, subtract octal 60 from each, resulting in two bcd digits of 0 through 9, and then *pack* the two bcd digits into one 8-bit byte. To convert back to ASCII from bcd, the two bcd digits are *unpacked* into two bytes and octal 60 is added to each. The following example shows this packing and unpacking operation.

Converting From ASCII to BCD

ASCII data:	8	9
ASCII values:	00111000	00111001
Adjust:	−00110000	−00110000
BCD:	00001000	00001001
Pack:		10001001

Converting From BCD to ASCII

Unpack:		01010111
Adjust:	00000101	00000111
ASCII values:	+00110000	+00110000
ASCII values:	00110101	00110111
ASCII data:	5	7

The second reason for using bcd or decimal representation is that mixed numbers containing integer and fractional parts, such as dollars and cents, can easily be manipulated without having to worry about scaling or keeping track of the decimal point. The whole problem of converting from a decimal point to a binary point, keeping track of the point, and then reconverting to a decimal number is not a trivial one. With bcd representation the decimal point is fixed in one place, and as long as accounting-type functions are performed decimal operations work quite well, at the expense of some inefficiency in add and subtract times and memory storage.

Floating-point operations offer a means to automatically keep track of the decimal point, extend the range of numbers that can be represented, and permit addition, subtraction, multiplication, and division of mixed numbers over a wide range without regard to scaling or decimal point location. The analogous form of floating-point representation in the real world is scientific notation. Scientific notation, as most of the readers are aware, represents numbers in the form $\pm$ X.XX $\times$ $10^{\pm E}$. A mixed number which can be either positive or negative ($\pm$ X.XX) is multiplied by ten raised to a positive or negative power. Some examples of the use of scientific notation to represent large and small numbers are given below.

Number	Number in Scientific Notation
−.00000123	-1.23×10^{-6}
+123777.6	$+1.23777 \times 10^{5}$
+1	$+1 \times 10^{0}$
−1	-1×10^{0}

The rules for working with numbers expressed in scientific notation are rather simple. To add or subtract two numbers in this form, change the numbers so that their exponents are equal, and then add or subtract the mixed number portion, retaining the same exponent.

Add $+1.23 \times 10^{-5}$ to -3.4×10^{-7}

1) $+1.23 \times 10^{-5} = +123.0 \times 10^{-7}$

2) Add $\quad +123.0 \times 10^{-7}$

$\quad\quad\quad -3.4 \quad\times 10^{-7}$

3) Result = $+119.6 \times 10^{-7}$

To multiply or divide two numbers in scientific notation, the exponents do not have to be equal; the mixed numbers are multiplied or divided and the exponents are either added (multiplication) or subtracted (division). When dividing, the exponent of the divisor is subtracted from the exponent of the dividend.

Multiply $+1.23 \times 10^{-5}$ by $-1.1 \times 10^{+7}$

1) Multiply mixed numbers $\quad\quad +1.23$

$\quad\quad\quad\quad\quad\quad\quad\quad \times -1.1$

$\quad\quad\quad\quad\quad\quad\quad\quad \overline{-1.353}$

2) Add exponents $\quad\quad\quad\quad -5$

$\quad\quad\quad\quad\quad\quad\quad +(+7)$

$\quad\quad\quad\quad\quad\quad\quad \overline{+2}$

3) Result = $-1.353 \times 10^{+2}$

Divide $-4.5 \times 10^{+10}$ by $-2.25 \times 10^{+12}$

1) Divide mixed numbers $\quad -4.5/-2.25 = +2$

2) Subtract divisor exponent from dividend exponent

$$\begin{array}{r} +10 \\ -(+12) \\ \hline -2 \end{array}$$

3) Result $= +2 \times 10^{-2}$

The software floating-point routines found in microcomputers emulate the scientific operations above. An operand input in ASCII format is first converted to a floating-point number similar to scientific notation form. Two operands can be added with a floating-point add routine, subtracted with a floating-point subtract routine, multiplied by a floating-point multiply routine, and divided by a floating-point divide routine. When all floating-point arithmetic has been accomplished a floating-point number can be reconverted to ASCII format. A typical ASCII input or output format for floating-point numbers is the form $\pm$X.XXXXE$\pm$YY where the mixed number is $\pm$X.XXXX and the exponent (power of ten) is $\pm$YY. Typically about 7 decimal digits may be in the mixed number and the exponent may be -99 to $+99$, allowing a great range of numbers to be expressed in this format. (It has been estimated that 10^{+99} *exceeds* by a factor of ten the number of different instructions in the next generation of microprocessors, for example!)

Internal representation of the floating-point number consists of a fractional part and an exponent. Although the format of the floating-point number is not standardized from one microcomputer to the next, a typical format might be as shown in Fig. 22-1. The floating-point number is held in four bytes. The sign of the fractional part is the msb of byte 0. The fraction is a binary fraction of the form .XXXXXXXXXXXXXXXXXXXXXXXX$_2$. The equivalent decimal fraction would contain about seven decimal digits, as the number of bits required to hold one decimal digit is about $3\frac{1}{2}$. The fraction is held in bytes 1, 2, and 3 in triple-precision format. The exponent is not base ten, but is base 16. In addition, the exponent is in *excess 64* form. An exponent value of 0000000_2 to 1111111_2 represents -64 through $+63$, respectively. The exponent value is changed to excess 64 form by adding 1000000_2 to the true value. This facilitates binary adds and subtracts of bytes 0 and 1.

SIGN OF FRACTION
EXCESS 64 EXPONENT
FRACTION

±SEEEEEEE	FFFFFFFF	FFFFFFFF	FFFFFFFF
BYTE 0	BYTE 1	BYTE 2	BYTE 3

In this format, the greatest number that can be represented is $+.FFFFFF_{16} \times 16^{+63}$, which is approximately 16^{+63} or 10^{+76}. The smallest number that can be represented is $-.000001 \times 16^{-64}$, which is identical with -1×16^{-70} or approximately -1×10^{-84}.

The floating-point add or subtract routines would operate in much the same fashion as manual methods used with scientific notation. The exponents of both operands would have to be equal for the add or subtract to be done, so the fraction of the operand with the larger exponent is shifted a hex digit at a time to the left while the exponent is decremented by one until the two exponents match. It is possible that one of the operands is out of the range of the other, and in this case the operation would be meaningless. If the exponents can be made equal, the add or subtract is performed in triple-precision on the fractional part of the floating-point number, and the result retains the adjusted exponent value. Multiplication and division routines simply add or subtract the exponents and multiply or divide the fractional parts in triple-precision.

The above discussion is a very broad coverage on floating-point representation. The reader is advised to look in other reference material or listings that provide further information or listings of complete floating-point routines.

DECIMAL ARITHMETIC—8080

The following routine illustrates the conversion of two four-digit ASCII operands to two two-byte bcd operands and the decimal addition of the two. The first operand in ASCII is in location BUF1 through BUF1+3 and the second is in locations BUF2 through BUF2+3. The comments field shows the contents of the A register before and after the DAA instruction.

```
DCADD   LXI     H,BUF1      POINT TO FIRST OPERAND
        CALL    PACK        PACK INTO BUF1, BUF1+1
        LXI     H,BUF2      POINT TO SECOND OPERAND
        CALL    PACK        PACK INTO BUF2, BUF2+1
        LXI     H,BUF2+1    POINT TO 2ND OPERAND LS
        LDA     BUF1+1      GET TWO LS BCD DIGITS
        ADD     M           ADD OPERANDS
        DCX     H           POINT TO 2ND OPERANDS MS
        DAA                 DECIMAL ADJUST
        STA     RES+1       SAVE RESULT LS
        LDA     BUF1        GET TWO MS BCD DIGITS
        ADC     M           ADD OPERANDS
        DAA                 DECIMAL ADJUST
        STA     RES         SAVE RESULT MS
        .
        .
```

```
PACK    MOV   A,M        GET MS DIGIT
        SUI   060        CONVERT TO BCD
        CALL  ROT        SHIFT LEFT 4
        MOV   M,A        SAVE
        INX   H          BUMP POINTER
        MOV   A,M        GET 2ND DIGIT
        SUI   060        CONVERT TO BCD
        MOV   M,A        SAVE
        INX   H          BUMP POINTER
        MOV   A,M        GET 3RD DIGIT
        SUI   060        CONVERT TO BCD
        CALL  ROT        SHIFT LEFT 4
        MOV   M,A        SAVE
        INX   H          BUMP POINTER
        MOV   A,M        GET 4TH DIGIT
        SUI   060        CONVERT TO BCD
        MOV   M,A        SAVE
        CALL  MERGE      MERGE BCD DIGITS
        RET              RETURN
          .
          .
MERGE   MOV   A,M        4TH DIGIT
        DCX   H          POINT TO 3RD
        ORA   M          NOW 3RD AND 4TH BCD
        MOV   B,A        SAVE
        DCX   H          POINT TO 2ND
        MOV   A,M        GET 2ND
        DCX   H          POINT TO 1ST
        ORA   M          NOW 1ST AND 2ND BCD
        MOV   M,A        STORE RESULT IN BUFX
        INX   H          POINT TO BUFX+1
        MOV   M,B        STORE RESULT IN BUFX+1
        RET
          .
          .
ROT     RLC              ROTATE (A) LEFT 4 BITS
        RLC
        RLC
        RLC
        RET              RETURN
```

There are several subroutines used. ROT rotates the contents of the A
register 4 bits left. MERGE merges the four bcd digits in four bytes of
the buffer into the first two bytes of the buffer. Before MERGE is
called, the four bcd digits are aligned as follows:

```
        BUFX+0   DDDD0000    FIRST BCD DIGIT
            +1   0000DDDD    SECOND BCD DIGIT
            +2   DDDD0000    THIRD BCD DIGIT
            +3   0000DDDD    FOURTH BCD DIGIT
```

PACK converts each ASCII digit in BUFX through BUFX+3 to bcd values aligned as shown above for MERGE to use. PACK calls both MERGE and ROT. The main routine DCADD adds the two ls bcd digits in BUF2+1 to the two ls bcd digits in BUF1+1 and, after the decimal adjust, puts the result in RES+1. It then adds the two ms bcd digits in BUF2 with the two ms digits in BUF1 *with carry,* does a decimal adjust, and puts the result in RES. The code could have been shortened considerably, but this will give the reader an idea of not only the DAA operation, but the conversion and unpacking operations as well.

DECIMAL ARITHMETIC—6800

The opposite operation from the above example, unpacking and converting a bcd result, is shown for the 6800. Here the bcd operands are two bytes in length (4 bcd digits) each and are located in OPER1,OPER1+1 and OPER2,OPER2+1. The result of the decimal add is to go into BUF through BUF+3 in ASCII form, ms digit of the result first.

```
DCADD   LDAA   OPER1+1    FIRST OP LS
        ADDA   OPER2+1    SECOND OP LS
        DAA               DECIMAL ADJUST A
        STA    BUF+2      SAVE RESULT
        LDAA   OPER1      FIRST OP MS
        ADCA   OPER2      SECOND OP MS (W/C)
        DAA               DECIMAL ADJUST A
        TAB               SAVE RESULT
        LSRB
        LSRB
        LSRB
        LSRB              ALIGN FIRST DIGIT
        ANDA   #$F        GET BCD DIGIT
        ANDB   #$F        GET BCD DIGIT
        ADDA   #@60       CONVERT TO ASCII
        ADDB   #@60       CONVERT TO ASCII
        STAB   BUF        STORE FIRST DIGIT
        STAA   BUF+1      STORE 2ND DIGIT
        LDA    BUF+2      RESTORE LS RESULT
        TAB               FOR SHIFT
        LSRB
        LSRB
        LSRB
        LSRB              ALIGN THIRD DIGIT
        ANDA   #$F        GET BCD DIGIT
        ANDB   #$F        GET BCD DIGIT
        ADDA   #@60       CONVERT TO ASCII
        ADDB   #@60       CONVERT TO ASCII
```

```
STAB    BUF+2       STORE THIRD DIGIT
STAA    BUF+3       STORE FOURTH DIGIT
.
.
```

Here no subroutines were used. The decimal adjust was done after each add, and the second add was an add with carry to pick up any carry from the lower-order bcl digit position. Each group of two digits of the result was then loaded into the A and B accumulators, properly shifted to a right justified position, ANDed to mask out any garbage, converted to an ASCII digit by the addition of octal 60, and stored in the buffer in preparation for printout.

DECIMAL ARITHMETIC—6502

The 6502 differs from both the 6800 and 8080 in that it has a decimal flag that can be set or reset by the SED and CLD instructions. If the decimal flag is set, then the 6502 will *always* perform decimal addition or *subtraction*. This means that if a long series of decimal adds or subtracts is to be performed there will not have to be an explicit decimal adjust after each operation. Decimal mode continues as long as the decimal flag is set. When reset, the arithmetic and logic unit performs binary addition and subtraction.

The code to perform decimal addition on two four-digit bcd operands is shown below. The operands are in OPER1,OPER1+1 and OPER2,OPER2+1 and the result goes to RES and RES+1.

```
DCADD   SED                 SET DECIMAL MODE
        LDA    OPER1+1      LS OPERAND 1
        CLC                 CLEAR CARRY
        ADC    OPER2+1      LS OPERAND 2
        STA    RES+1        LS RESULT
        LDA    OPER1        MS OPERAND 1
        ADC    OPER2        MS RESULT
        STA    RES          MS RESULT
        CLD                 CLEAR DECIMAL MODE
        .
        .
```

The code to perform bcd subtraction is similar, but the carry flag *must be set* before the first (least significant) subtract takes place. Here the operands are named identically to the above example. On further subtractions the borrow is propagated from the lower-order subtractions automatically.

```
DCSUB   SED                 DECIMAL MODE
        LDA    OPER1+1      LS OPERAND 1
        SEC                 SET CARRY
```

```
SBC    OPER2+1    SUBTRACT LS OP 2
STA    RES+1      SAVE RESULT
LDA    OPER1      MS OPERAND 1
SBC    OPER2      MS OPERAND 2
STA    RES        MS RESULT
CLD               CLEAR DECIMAL MODE
```

.
.

I/O Operations

This chapter will concern itself not so much with the I/O devices used on microcomputers themselves, or their controllers, but the approach used in software to communicate with various types of I/O devices. One of the reasons for avoiding detailed descriptions of the I/O device controllers is that, just like the case of the *Enterprise's* battle computers, there is not a great deal of standardization among the devices. We will therefore separate the device and device controller from the rest of the system by discussing the software I/O driver and other software that communicates with the I/O driver. In addition, interrupt processing and reentrancy methods will be discussed.

Chapter 10 discussed I/O via cpu registers a byte at a time and I/O via the DMA (Direct Memory Access). The first method is called *programmed I/O* and the second *DMA I/O*. The less complex I/O and lower-speed I/O devices would generally use programmed I/O, while the high-speed I/O devices would use a combination of programmed I/O and DMA. In the latter case programmed I/O is used to pass arguments for control and receive status relating to the actual transfer of data, which is done via DMA. Regardless of the device, the basic software routine for communication with the device and device controller is called the *software driver*. It is essentially a subroutine that contains the necessary code to handle all communication with the particular I/O device, which is effectively all programmed I/O, since the DMA operates in a transparent manner to the program.

The more complex the I/O device the more complex the I/O driver and the greater the reason for having just one set of code to handle all communication with the device, rather than duplicating code each time the device is used in the program. In the simplest case, a Teletype or Teletype-like device like a TV Typewriter, the primary function that the Teletype I/O driver performs is to check the ready flag in the I/O controller to determine if there is a character waiting to be input or to determine if the last output character has been completely sent to the device. The code for these functions would be similar to the following, written in 6502 assembly language.

```
* TTY OUTPUT ROUTINE
TTYOT  LDA  TTY       LOAD TTY STATUS
       AND  MASK      GET READY STATUS BIT
       BEQ  TTYOT     LOOP IF NOT READY
       TYA
       STA  TTYA      OUTPUT CHARACTER
       RTS            RETURN
* TTY INPUT ROUTINE
TTYIN  LDA  TTY       LOAD TTY STATUS
       AND  MASK1     GET STATUS BIT
       BEQ  TTYIN     LOOP IF NO INPUT
       LDA  TTYA
       RTS            RETURN
```

In the output routine, the ASCII character to be output is in the Y index register. A check is first made of the ready status of the TTY controller by reading the status by the LDA instruction. The LDA uses the I/O address of the TTY controller that returns status information. If the status bit is not set, as, for example, it would not be if the previous character was still being output (remember it may take tens of thousands of instruction times to finish I/O on one character), the routine loops back to TTYOT. When the TTY is ready the status bit is set, the TYA transfers the ASCII character in the Y register to the accumulator, and an output is done by the STA instruction, which uses another address for the TTY to effect the transfer of the character. The TTY input routine is similar, except that it uses a different mask to check the input status bit, and, of course, does an input by an LDA.

The driver shown above is a "wait-for-complete" type of I/O driver, as the code loops on the status check until the device controller becomes ready, at which point the next character is read in or sent out. An alternative approach, as previously discussed, would be an *interrupt-driven* output routine in which the ready status would initiate an interrupt. The interrupt processing routine would then process the next character until the last character in the buffer was handled. Although TTY routines are usually not interrupt driven, there is no reason why they shouldn't be, and the following example gives the general approach. Suppose that a message of thirty or forty ASCII characters is to be output to a TTY. The message is a periodic report on the status of the system and is output every 10 seconds while normal processing continues. If the system is monitoring *real-time* data and cannot be shut down to loop in the I/O routine for the three or four seconds it takes to output the message, then an interrupt-driven I/O could well be used. In this case, the first character would be output by the I/O routine in the same fashion as above. The interrupts would then be *armed* in the TTY controller (this is a command which tells the controller that the pending I/O will be on an interrupt basis), the interrupt flag in the cpu will be set by the "set interrupt flag" instruction, and the I/O driver would then return to the calling program. The program that called the I/O driver would then continue processing real-time data. When the character was completely transmitted to the TTY, the ready status would cause an external interrupt to the cpu. If the interrupts were enabled at that point the automatic transfer to the interrupt routine for the TTY would be entered. If the interrupts were not enabled in the cpu precisely at that time, the interrupt would occur when the interrupt flag in the cpu was again set. It is perfectly permissible to enable and disable interrupts by turning the cpu interrupt flag off and on at various times. Any pending interrupt will be remembered and will cause an interrupt when the flag is again set.

When the interrupt routine is entered, the environment is saved as previously described. All volatile cpu registers and flags are either pushed into the stack automatically or under program control, dependent upon the microprocessor. The interrupt routine then picks up the next character from the message buffer, and, if it is not a terminating character, outputs the character to the TTY, arms the TTY interrupt, enables the system interrupts, and returns to the interrupted point after restoring the environment. Identical interrupt processing occurs for each of the characters to be output. When the last character has been output, detected by either a special terminating character at the end of the message string, or by decrementing a count to zero, the TTY interrupt routine sets a software flag indicating that I/O has been completed for the message and does not initiate any new I/O. At some point, perhaps when the next system message is to be output, the main program checks this flag to determine that the last message was properly output, resets the flag, and starts the next message by calling the interrupt-driven TTY I/O driver.

The interrupt-driven I/O utilized an I/O buffer to hold a string of ASCII characters to be output. I/O buffers are commonly used for every type of I/O, and are a necessity for DMA transfers where data to be transferred must be blocked in one contiguous set of memory locations for the automatic transfer. A convenient-sized buffer for a Teletype would be the maximum length of one Teletype line, or 72 bytes. Buffers for tv displays are commonly 32 or 64 characters long for ASCII oriented displays and a thousand or more bytes long for graphics type displays. In the latter case the buffer in memory represents the entire matrix of points or characters that will be displayed on the screen. In the case of an audio cassette interface, the buffer may be *variable-length* as the number of bytes written to the tape does not have to be a specific length which is related to the physical characteristics of the I/O device. Buffers for floppy disc, on the other hand, are conveniently made the same length as the *sector* on the floppy disc. All writes and reads will be the same number of characters, at least on a sector basis; this is an example of a *fixed-length* buffer.

How many buffers are required? As many as it takes to perform the I/O. Predefined messages are assembled in a message area and in effect are their own buffers. The location of each message is passed to the I/O driver for output either in a wait-for-complete or interrupt driven operation. The assembler generates the necessary ASCII characters automatically. An example of a set of messages for the 6800 are shown below.

MSG1	FCC	/QUICKLY/
MSG2	FCC	/WATSON/
MSG3	FCC	/THE GAME'S/
MSG4	FCC	/AFOOT!/

Strings of characters which are constructed dynamically, such as an assembler listing output, must be put into one or more buffer areas. Typically there might be one buffer for listing output, one for source line input, and one for assembler object output. The numbers of these are not too important, as the buffer lengths involved are small. When large buffers are required, however, as in the case of video graphics, cassette tape *records,* and floppy disc records, only one or two should be used at a time to save memory. An example of an advantageous use of two buffers would be a *double-buffering* type of I/O. Double buffering would be used to speed up the I/O by allowing a DMA or interrupt-driven I/O to proceed from one buffer while the program is processing data and filling in the other buffer. When the I/O is complete for the first buffer, the I/O for the second buffer is started, and the program now processes data into the first buffer. In this way processing and I/O can be overlapped. This type of buffering is sometimes called *ping-pong* buffering for obvious reasons.

A slightly more elaborate I/O driver for Teletype I/O would require an address defining the start of the I/O buffer, and possibly a flag defining whether the operation was to be wait-for-complete or interrupt driven. The I/O buffer would contain a terminating character such as a null (zero) or might contain the number of characters to be output as the first byte of the I/O buffer. The 8080 call to such a driver would appear as shown below.

```
LXI    B,MSG1    POINT TO MESSAGE
XRA    A         ZERO A FOR WAIT FLAG
CALL   TTYOT     OUTPUT MESSAGE
 .               CONTINUE PROCESSING
 .
```

As might be expected, there is a kind of creeping elegance that one notices as one thinks of more and more functions that an I/O driver could perform. Some of these are very much related to the I/O device and are required functions for operation of the I/O device. An audio cassette interface, for example, might provide a fast forward, fast reverse, read a record, and write a record function in addition to supplying status information about the device. These functions could be implemented in the I/O driver by passing the proper parameters from the calling program to the driver. In the cassette example, for instance, a block of I/O parameters might be passed to the cassette I/O driver by specifying the address of the parameter block. A typical example of the parameters would be:

IOPAR+0   Function: 0 = read, 1 = write, 2 = FF, 3 = reverse
IOPAR+1   Address of buffer for reads, writes
IOPAR+2   Interrupt flag: 0 = interrupt, 1 = wait
IOPAR+3   Status: holds status at end of operation

Naturally, the more complicated the I/O device, the more commands and status information that has to be passed, and probably the more complicated the I/O driver and number of parameters that must be passed. However, why limit the I/O driver to physical functions only? It might be nice to be able to find the nth record on the audio cassette tape, for example, or to skip n records, or to keep a directory of records on cassette. This is the creeping elegance effect and it is not necessarily a bad thing. In general, though, the reader is advised to implement logical I/O functions in the I/O driver with enough generality to enable the program to easily perform I/O on the device. Other, more elegant functions can be accomplished by *file manage* programs or monitor programs.

I/O OPERATIONS—8080

The 8080 IN and OUT instructions have been previously discussed in Chapter 10. They offer up to 256 unique I/O addresses without encroaching upon memory addresses. All programmed I/O is done using the IN and OUT. A sample Teletype I/O driver is shown as follows. Note that the I/O driver automatically supplies a carriage return, line feed by a call to the CRLF routine and that the output of the character string automatically terminates when a null (zero) is detected.

```
          CALL  CRLF      NEW LINE
          LXI   H,MSG1    OUTPUT TITLE
          CALL  TTYOT
            .
            .
            .
CRLF      LXI   H,CRBUF   POINT TO CRLF CHARACTERS
          CALL  TTYOT     OUTPUT CRLF
          RET
            .
            .
TTYOT     MOV   B,M       GET CHARACTER
          RZ              RETURN IF NULL
TTYO1     IN    TTYS      GET STATUS
          ANI   2         CHECK READY
          JZ    TTYO1     LOOP TILL READY
          MOV   A,B       CHARACTER
          OUT   TTYD      OUTPUT CHARACTER
          INX   H         BUMP CHARACTER POINTER
          JMP   TTYOT     GO FOR NEW CHARACTER
            .
            .
```

Teletype input is similarly handled. Termination on input may be on a terminate character, such as a carriage return or line feed, or could be after a specified number of characters, or either.

As the 8080 hardware implements an interrupt by jamming a RST instruction onto the data bus at a particular time, only the current contents of the program counter are saved at interrupt time. The remaining environment must be saved if any cpu flags or registers are to be used in the interrupt processing routine. The following code illustrates saving and restoring the environment in a typical interrupt processing routine. The interrupt is for vectored interrupt number one which causes a RST to location 8. Since eight locations are not sufficient to process the interrupt, the instruction in location 8 is a jump to the main body of the interrupt routine.

```
LOC 8         JMP   TTYIN     JUMP TO INT HANDLER
                .
                .
LOC N  TTYIN  DI              PREVENT FURTHER INT
              PUSH  PSW       SAVE A AND FLAGS
              PUSH  B         SAVE B,C
              PUSH  D         SAVE D,E
              PUSH  H         SAVE H,L
```

```
              .
              .
     POP    H          RESTORE H,L
     POP    D          RESTORE D,E
     POP    B          RESTORE B,C
     POP    PSW        RESTORE A, FLAGS
     EI                ENABLE INTERRUPTS
     RET               RETURN
```

Note that the first instruction disables further interrupts. This is optional if the system is set up to handle more than one interrupt simultaneously and there are no reentrancy problems. All cpu registers and the cpu flags are saved at the beginning of the interrupt processing routine and restored at the end before enabling interrupts and returning to the interrupted location. If some of the registers were not used in the interrupt routine, then there would be no need to save them except that one tends to forget that fact in subsequent modification of the program.

I/O OPERATIONS—6800

A TTY input routine that terminates either on a carriage return or after 8 characters is given below. As each character is input it is stored in the buffer area defined by the contents of the stack pointer. Since the buffer area is only 8 bytes long some protection must be provided to stop user input after 8 characters. Typically a routine such as this might be used to input commands to a system monitor.

```
            LDX    #BUFIN    ADDRESS OF INPUT BUFFER
            JSR    COMIN     GO TO INPUT DRIVER
            .                PROCESS COMMAND
            .
            .
COMIN       LDAB   #8        SETUP INDEX COUNT
LOOP        LDAA   TTYS      GET TTY STATUS
            ANDA   #4        TEST INPUT STATUS
            BEQ    LOOP      LOOP TILL DONE
            LDAA   TTYD      GET CHARACTER
            CMPA   #CR       TEST FOR CR
            BEQ    RET       RETURN IF CR
            STAA   X         STORE CHARACTER
            INX              BUMP BUFFER POINTER
            DECB             DECREMENT COUNT
            BNE    LOOP      GO FOR NEXT IF NOT DONE
RET         RTS              RETURN FROM SUBROUTINE
            .
            .
```

Interrupt handling is made considerably less tedious in the 6800 as all of the registers and flags are saved automatically when the interrupt occurs. No special actions are necessary in the interrupt routine to save the environment. The RTI, Return From Interrupt, instruction automatically restores the environment at the completion of interrupt processing.

Many of the microcomputers using the 6800 have an inherent monitor program in PROM. In some cases this is the Motorola MIKBUG program and in others it is the manufacturer's own monitor/debug package. Both types should offer Teletype and possibly other I/O driver programs that could be used to advantage by the programmer.

I/O OPERATIONS—6502

A routine to space n lines or n character positions on a Teletype is provided for the 6502 below. This type of routine could possibly be used for plotting data on a Teletype or alphanumeric display as coordinates of points given in x,y were converted to corresponding line positions and character positions. Entry is made to the routine with the accumulator holding the function; 0 is the function for line space, and 1 is the function for character position space. The x register holds the number of lines or character positions to space.

```
MAINP   LDA   #0       SETUP FOR LINE SPACE
        LDX   #20      SPACE 20 LINES
        JSR   SPACE    GO TO SPACE LINES
        .
        .
SPACE   LDY   #LF      LOAD LF CHARACTER
        CMP   #0       COMPARE FUNCTION
        BEQ   LOP1     GO IF LINE SPACE
        LDY   #BL      LOAD BLANK CHARACTER
LOP1    DEX            DECREMENT NUMBER
        BMI            GO IF DONE
LOOP    LDA   TTYS     LOAD STATUS
        AND   #2       TEST FOR READY
        BEQ   LOOP     LOOP TILL READY
        TYA            TRANSFER CHARACTER
        STA   TTYD     OUTPUT CHARACTER
        JMP   LOP1     GO FOR NEXT
        .
        .
```

When an interrupt occurs in the 6502, the address of the interrupted instruction (the contents of the PC) and the processor flags are automatically pushed into the stack. If the interrupt handling routine is to use any of the remaining cpu registers they must first be saved in the stack and then restored after the interrupt processing is over. The sequence for this is shown below. The contents of the other registers must first

```
INTHN   PHA     SAVE A
        TXA     GET  X
        PHA     SAVE X
        TYA     GET  Y
        PHA     SAVE Y
        .
        .
        .
        PLA     GET  Y
        TAY     RESTORE  Y
        PLA     GET  X
        TAX     RESTORE  X
        PLA     RESTORE  A
        RTI     RETURN  FROM  INTERRUPT
```

be transferred to the accumulator to enable a push to the stack in saving the registers and a similar transfer must be used in restoring the registers. The RTI pulls the processor flags and program counter from the stack automatically.

Putting It All Together

The chapters before this described commonly used assembly language programming techniques for the 8080, 6800, and 6502 microcomputers. By now the reader should have a fairly thorough understanding of how to perform basic programming operations. The only thing remaining is to take the basic techniques and to build upon them to implement a program or subroutine to perform broader functions. This chapter will attempt to explain how to do this, with the example of a line editor. A line editor, sometimes called a text editor, is a program that enables a user to create or modify assembly-language source *files*. A file is composed of *records* and records are composed, in this case, of character data. We'll specifically assume that the line editor to be implemented works with assembly-language source files made up of records of assembly language source lines. The lines may be one to 64 characters in length and are terminated by a carriage return. A file is composed of from one to any number of records and basically contains a set of records representing a complete program. The line editor will create a new source file on paper tape or cassette tape or will modify an old program on paper tape or cassette and produce a new version on either medium.

The line editor will receive commands that indicate the editing to be done from Teletype or TV Typewriter. The following are the valid commands:

1. +N,N   Delete line number N of the old file. Do not output to the new file.
2. +N,M   Delete line numbers N through M of the old file. Do not output to the new file.
3. +N   Output the current line of the old file through line N of the old file to the new file.

4. +N   Output the current line of the old file through line N of the old file to the new file. Then output new lines 1, 2, . . . , N to the new file.

LINE 1

LINE 2

.

LINE N

5. +E   End the edit by outputing the current line of the old file through the last line of the old file to the new file.

In addition to the edit commands above, the line editor initially inputs a command string that defines the old file device, the new file device, and the command device as follows:

/EDIT,O,N,C

Possible mnemonics for O are TTY or CAS. Possible mnemonics for N are TTY or CAS. Possible mnemonics for C are TTY or TVT. To edit from TTY paper tape to cassette using the TVT for edit commands, the user would type /EDIT,TTY,CAS,TVT followed by a carriage return. To delete lines 3 through 53 and to insert three new lines after line 67 of the old file, the commands would be:

+3,53
+67
(New line number 1)
(New line number 2)
(New line number 3)
+E

By defining the above specification for the line editor, we've already done one of the most important steps in producing any new set of programs—we've determined that our computer system can actually perform the task, and we've drawn up a workable set of guidelines on how the program is to function. There are many commercial programs that never reach this phase until 90 percent of the way through the project, if at all. In this case the problem of determining whether the system could do the task was trivial. There are no severe time constraints in executing the program and we'll assume that all equipment and interfaces function properly in addition to having a reasonable amount of memory, say 2K bytes. The specification of line editor commands was a bit more difficult. By gleaning the latest copies of some of the computer magazines and by looking at other reference material we decided that the above functions could be quite reasonably implemented. If they were not as exotic as some of the software packages currently offered, we know as least that our documentation will be superb and it will be easy to add to the program later to expand its capabilities (won't it?).

Having the basic functions firmly fixed, we can now go to the next step in implementing the program, determining what routines will be required. Some of these routines already exist, for we have kept a large library of routines in source language form on paper tape, along with listings describing each routine. Others we will have to create from scratch. Having in mind future projects, we'd best create routines that are general purpose in nature so that they can be used in other programs. Some of the code, of course, will be unique to the line editor and will never be able to be reused, but we'll try to write code in the generic form whenever possible. Now let's see what we'll need. We'll obviously need a Teletype I/O driver. Hmmm, we have one in the library that reads a line of characters terminated by a carriage return or 64 characters, and writes a line of n characters. In our system the paper tape reader is mechanically linked to the keyboard, so that will take care of reading or punching paper tape as well. Another routine that will be required is a cassette I/O driver. We'll have to write that one, having just acquired a 187 byte per second beauty. The TV Typewriter I/O driver also exists.

Now let's see. A routine for converting ASCII line numbers to binary is required. Possible other routines would be a routine to scan a line of arguments *delimited* by commas to find the two arguments in the line and a routine to search for the nth record. We may not add the search routine or the argument subroutines at this point, however. They can be done at a later date when we get more experience in string manipulation techniques. The current subroutines we now need for the program are:

1. TTY I/O Driver
2. Cassette I/O Driver
3. TV Typewriter I/O Driver
4. ASCII decimal to binary conversion routine.

Now that the basic routines required have been determined, let's rough out a general flow of the program. Flowcharts aren't really required at this point unless one works better by describing things in that fashion. The actions which are listed below are roughly the things that happen:

1. Program starts. Variables initialized, things generally reset.
2. Title printed on TTY. Request made for /EDIT command.
3. READ in /EDIT command. If in error, repeat; otherwise store old file type, new file type, and command device.
4. Read in edit command from command device using command device driver. If proper sequence, syntax continues; otherwise output error message and go to 4.

5. Strip arguments from command.
   a. If +N type, output current line from old file through N to new file, reading one line at a time from the old file device.
   b. If +N,M type, read in old lines *n* through *m* from old file device a line at a time. Do not output to the new file device.
   c. If +N,N type do the same as step 5b.
   d. If the first character is not a PLUS output this line to new file device as a new line.
   e. If +E, read in current old lines through end of old file, one line at a time. As each is read, output to new file device. Then go to step 1.

Implicit in these steps are things like checking line numbers to see that they have not already gone by, error message printout, checks on the validity of data from the various I/O devices, and the like.

Now that the rough sequence of steps has been listed a more formal flowchart can be drawn up using a flowcharting template, your own flowcharting symbols, or a series of steps in finer detail. The only consideration for doing things in standardized fashion is that occasionally you may want other programmers to work from your flow diagram, and they may experience some trouble if they are not in standard fashion. Included in the charts will be a reference to three buffer areas, the old line buffer, 64 characters long, the new line buffer, 64 characters long, and the command buffer, 64 characters long or less. Once the flow diagrams have been done, it's probably best to sit back and say, "Have I covered every possibility?" and, like the worried mother, "Where did I go wrong?" It will save a lot of time later.

Once the reader has checked and rechecked the flow diagrams, coding can begin. For those readers without assemblers, the sequence is almost identical with those with assemblers. In each case the symbolic source lines are printed with comments. Leave spaces between each line for additions, the more spaces the better. Locations are assigned symbolic names in both cases. The use of comments cannot be too strongly urged. Except when it is completely clear what the instruction is doing, each source line should have a comment describing the code. In addition, code should be blocked off by comment lines to make separate routines of code recognizable. An example would be:

```
*******************************************************
*              ASCII TO DECIMAL              *
*                CONVERSION                  *
*******************************************************
*   THIS ROUTINE CONVERTS UP TO 6 ASCII DIGITS
*   INTO A 16-BIT BINARY VALUES. ENTER WITH
```

After the code has been checked and rechecked (desk checked), the assembler-less programmers can hand assemble, while the programmers with assemblers can let the assembler perform the work. In either case there will probably be errors, necessitating reassembly by hand or machine. When you are certain the program code is perfect, then it is time to start debugging.

Unfortunately, in most cases the program will not run perfectly the first time. In fact, if it is large, it probably won't run perfectly the tenth time. When debugging, it is sometimes helpful to debug a small section of the code at a time. Try parameters that reflect a typical value and then values that are the extremes. For example, in a table look-up, try a value that turns out to be at the middle of the table, followed by values at the extreme top and bottom of the table. The entire debugging process will be greatly speeded up by the time spent in desk checking. When errors are found in the code, it may be better to avoid reassembling and simply *patch* the code, changing the instruction to the proper op code and/or address by overwriting the first version. Sometimes this may mean jumping out to a *patch area* where additional code may be inserted, and then jumping back to the instruction following the patched jump, analogous to jumping out to a subroutine. It is often convenient to leave NOPs at appropriate points in the program that can be patched with code if necessary.

Once the program has been debugged and various test cases tried and the programmer is fairly certain it works, then a final version of the source code can be produced and saved on paper tape, cassette, or handwritten copies, along with the specifications on the use of the program. In many cases this will not be the final version, as is the case with most software "released" by manufacturers. There always seems to be one combination of things that has not been encountered. Typically this bug results in destroying the program when one is running at two a.m. with no back-up system. The bugs, however, *will* diminish with each version of the program.

While the above is a very brief sketch of the process of designing, writing, and debugging a program, it is hoped that the reader will expand upon it by going over existing programs from manufacturer's listings, manufacturer's documentation, programs printed in computer magazines, and other programming reference books. It is difficult to define a programming style and probably the best way to acquire it is by emulation of the techniques used by other programmers. Some programs just *look good* with many comments, modularity of routines, proper placement of the main body of the code, subroutines and buffers, and code that is easy to follow. It is possible to produce programs similar to this and yet still have a great deal of fun while implementing assembly-language code.

PART

4

Programming
Algorithms

Programming Algorithms

This chapter provides commonly used subroutines for microcomputers based on the 8080, 6800, and 6502. Each routine is described in six paragraphs. The name of the routine is usually related to the function it performs. FILLD is *FILL D*ata, for example. The function of the routine is briefly described in the next paragraph. The third paragraph describes the calling sequence of the subroutine. It specifies where the arguments for the subroutine are stored, and where results of the subroutine are to be found. When memory locations rather than cpu registers are used to hold input arguments and output results, the memory locations are usually specified as page 0 locations for the 6800 and 6502. The next paragraph describes which registers are destroyed in the operation of the subroutine. In some cases no registers are used and the subroutine may be called with the contents of all registers returned intact. In other cases some or all registers are utilized by the subroutine and must be saved in the stack before the subroutine is called if the register contents must be preserved.

The last section of each subroutine is a complete program listing of the subroutine. A complete set of symbolic assembly language code is listed under the Label, Operand, Arguments, and Comments columns. Standard microprocessor manufacturer's mnemonics are used for operands and arguments. Labels are limited to five characters. The Loc column specifies the memory locations that the subroutine is to occupy. 8080 subroutines start at location 000, 6800 subroutines start at location 100_{16}, and 6502 subroutines start at location 200_{16}. The Contents column shows the equivalent machine language code for the subroutine assembled for those memory locations. Relocating the subroutine to another portion of memory should be straightforward. When page 0 locations are referenced, they are designated by a two-character value in the machine code, such as XX, YY, ZZ, or WW. In some cases a subroutine will call another subroutine. In these cases the address of the called subroutine is represented by XX XX with an asterisk indicating that the actual address must be filled in by the user. When relocating the code for these subroutines, pay particular attention to properly changing addresses. Many instructions will remain unchanged, but those instructions that specify a direct memory address must be changed to reflect the new location of the subroutine. 8080 direct addresses are in the instruction least significant byte of the address first, followed by the high-order byte, as are 6502 addresses. 6800 addresses have the most significant byte of the address first, followed by the least significant byte. In general, a one-byte or two-byte instruction will not have to be altered if the program is moved, while a three-byte instruction will require a recomputation of the address. In general, all double-precision variables are in memory with the most significant byte followed by the least significant byte.

It is hoped that these subroutines will provide a convenient way to implement commonly used functions in the reader's microcomputer and also offer a comparison of the implementation of the functions on the three types of microprocessors.

SUBROUTINES

SCOMP   Simple Compare for 8080
SHIFT   Shift Subroutine for 8080
SHIFT   Shift Subroutine for 6800
SHIFT   Shift Subroutine for 6502
TIME   Timing Loop for 8080
TIME   Timing Loop for 6800
TIME   Timing Loop for 6502
UNSPM   Unsigned Single-Precision Multiply for 8080
UNSPM   Unsigned Single-Precision Multiply for 6800
UNSPM   Unsigned Single-Precision Multiply for 6502
UNSPD   Unsigned Single-Precision Divide for 8080
UNSPD   Unsigned Single-Precision Divide for 6800
UNSPD   Unsigned Single-Precision Divide for 6502
MPADD   Multiple-Precision Add for 8080
MPADD   Multiple-Precision Add for 6800
MPADD   Multiple-Precision Add for 6502
MPSUB   Multiple-Precision Subtract for 8080
MPSUB   Multiple-Precision Subtract for 6800
MPSUB   Multiple-Precision Subtract for 6502
ASBXB   ASCII Binary to Binary Subroutine for 8080
ASBXB   ASCII Binary to Binary Subroutine for 6800
ASBXB   ASCII Binary to Binary Subroutine for 6502

ASDXB	ASCII Decimal to Binary Subroutine for 8080
ASDXB	ASCII Decimal to Binary Subroutine for 6800
ASDXB	ASCII Decimal to Binary Subroutine for 6502
ASHXB	ASCII Hexadecimal to Binary Subroutine for 8080
ASHXB	ASCII Hexadecimal to Binary Subroutine for 6800
ASHXB	ASCII Hexadecimal to Binary Subroutine for 6502
ASOXB	ASCII Octal to Binary Subroutine for 8080
BXASB	Binary to ASCII Binary Subroutine for 8080
BXASB	Binary to ASCII Binary Subroutine for 6800
BXASB	Binary to ASCII Binary Subroutine for 6502
BXASD	Binary to ASCII Decimal Subroutine for 8080
BXASD	Binary to ASCII Decimal Subroutine for 6800
BXASD	Binary to ASCII Decimal Subroutine for 6502
BXASO	Binary to ASCII Octal Subroutine for 8080
BXASH	Binary to ASCII Hexadecimal Subroutine for 8080
BXASH	Binary to ASCII Hexadecimal Subroutine for 6800
BXASH	Binary to ASCII Hexadecimal Subroutine for 6502
MVDAT	Move Data Subroutine for 8080
MVDAT	Move Data Subroutine for 6800
MVDAT	Move Data Subroutine for 6502
FILLD	Fill Data Subroutine for 8080
FILLD	Fill Data Subroutine for 6800
FILLD	Fill Data Subroutine for 6502
COMST	Compare String Subroutine for 8080
COMST	Compare String Subroutine for 6800
COMST	Compare String Subroutine for 6502
SRTAB	Search Table Subroutine for 8080
SRTAB	Search Table Subroutine for 6800
SRTAB	Search Table Subroutine for 6502
RANDM	Random Number Generator for 8080
RANDM	Random Number Generator for 6800
RANDM	Random Number Generator for 6502

SCOMP 8080

I. *Name:* SCOMP   Simple Compare for 8080

II. *Description:* Compares two 8-bit operands in the A and B registers to find (A < B), (A = B), or (A > B). The
comparison is an unsigned compare. (Both numbers treated as 8-bit unsigned values.) Reentrant.

III. *Calling Sequence:* (A) = Operand A

           (B) = Operand B

           CALL   SCOMP

           (A<B return)

           (A=B return)

           (A>B return)

IV. *Volatility:* All registers returned with original contents.

V. *Notes:* By setting up the proper jumps at the three return points
this subroutine will test for A<B, A≦B, A=B, A>B, or
A≧B.

Loc	Contents	Label	Operand	Arguments	Comments
000	270	SCOMP	CMP	B	COMPARE (A)—(B)
001	341		POP	H	RETURN ADDRESS
002	312 013 000		JZ	EQUAL	GO IF EQUAL
005	332 016 000		JC	LTHAN	GO IF LESS THAN
010	043		INX	H	GREATER THAN
011	043		INX	H	
012	043		INX	H	
013	043	EQUAL	INX	H	EQUAL
014	043		INX	H	
015	043		INX	H	
016	351	LTHAN	PCHL		RETURN

SHIFT 8080

I. *Name:* SHIFT   Shift Subroutine for 8080

II. *Description:* Shifts the contents of (H,L) any given number of bit positions to the right or left in a rotate type of shift. Reentrant.

III. *Calling Sequence:* (A) = Number of shifts, 1 through 15. If this number is positive, shift is right shift, if negative, shift is left shift.

(H,L) = Double-precision value to be rotated.

CALL   SHIFT

[Return with (H,L) shifted]

IV. *Volatility:* All registers returned with original contents except A, H,L, and B.

V. *Notes:* This routine enables user to perform double-precision shifts in either direction. No checks are made for shifts greater than 15 or shifts of 0. Logical shifts may be performed by calling this routine for the shift and then masking out the appropriate bits.

Loc	Contents	Label	Operand	Arguments	Comments
000	107	SHIFT	MOV	B,A	
001	247		ANA	A	TEST FOR DIRECTION
002	372 024 000		JM	ROTLF	GO IF LEFT SHIFT
005	005	ROTRT	DCR	B	DECREMENT INDEX
006	370		RM		RETURN IF DONE
007	345		PUSH	H	SAVE PARTIAL RESULT
010	175		MOV	A,L	L TO A
011	037		RAR		SETUP CARRY
012	341		POP	H	RESTORE PARTIAL RES
013	174		MOV	A,H	
014	037		RAR		ROTATE MS BYTE
015	147		MOV	H,A	RESTORE MS
016	175		MOV	A,L	
017	037		RAR		ROTATE LS BYTE
020	157		MOV	L,A	RESTORE LS
021	303 005 000		JMP	ROTRT	CONTINUE
024	005	ROTLF	DCR	B	ADJUST FOR INDEX
025	004	ROTL1	INR	B	INCREMENT INDEX
026	310		RZ		RETURN IF DONE
027	345		PUSH	H	SAVE PARTIAL RESULT
030	174		MOV	A,H	H TO A
031	027		RAL		SETUP CARRY
032	341		POP	H	RESTORE PARTIAL RES
033	175		MOV	A,L	
034	027		RAL		ROTATE LS BYTE
035	157		MOV	L,A	RESTORE
036	174		MOV	A,H	
037	027		RAL		ROTATE MS BYTE
040	147		MOV	H,A	RESTORE
041	303 025 000		JMP	ROTL1	CONTINUE

SHIFT 6800

I. *Name:* SHIFT   Double-Precision Shift Subroutine for 6800

II. *Description:* Shifts the contents of A,B any given number of bit positions to the right or left in a rotate type of shift. Reentrant.

III. *Calling Sequence:* (X) = Number of shifts, 1 through 15. If this number is positive, shift is right shift, if negative, shift is left shift.

   (A,B) = Double-precision number to be rotated.

   JSR   SHIFT

   (Return with A,B shifted)

IV. *Volatility:* All registers used.

V. *Notes:* This routine enables the user to perform double-length shifts in either direction. No checks are made for shifts greater than 15 or shifts of 0. Logical shifts may be performed by calling this routine and then masking out the appropriate bits.

Loc	Contents	Label	Operand	Arguments	Comments
100	8C 00 00	SHIFT	CPX	#0	TEST DIRECTION
103	2B 0B		BMI	SHFLF	GO IF LEFT SHIFT
105	08		INX		ADJUST
106	09	LOOP	DEX		DECREMENT COUNT
107	27 12		BEQ	DONE	GO IF DONE
109	36		PSHA		
10A	46		RORA		SET CARRY
10B	32		PULA		
10C	56		RORB		RIGHT SHIFT WITH C
10D	46		RORA		ROTATE
10E	20 F6		BRA	LOOP	CONTINUE
110	09	SHFLF	DEX		ADJUST FOR TEST
111	08	LOP1	INX		INCREMENT COUNT
112	27 07		BEQ	DONE	GO IF DONE
114	37		PSHB		
115	59		ROLB		SET CARRY
116	33		PULB		
117	49		ROLA		LEFT SHIFT WITH C
118	59		ROLB		
119	20 F6		BRA	LOP1	CONTINUE
11B	39	DONE	RTS		RETURN

SHIFT 6502

I. *Name:* SHIFT   Double-Precision Shift Subroutine for 6502

II. *Description:* Shifts the contents of two memory locations, treated as a 16-bit double-precision number, any given number of bit positions to the right or left in a rotate type of shift.

III. *Calling Sequence:* (X) = Number of shifts, 1 through 15. If this number is positive, shift is right shift, if negative, shift is left shift.

(MSDP,LSDP) = Double-precision number to be rotated (Z Page)

JSR   SHIFT

[Return with (MSDP,LSDP) shifted]

IV. *Volatility:* All registers used.

V. *Notes:* This routine enables the user to perform double-length shifts in either direction. No checks are made for shifts greater than 15 or shifts of 0. Logical shifts may be performed by calling this routine and then masking out the appropriate bits.

Loc	Contents	Label	Operand	Arguments	Comments
200	E0 00	SHIFT	CPX	#0	FIND DIRECTION
202	30 20		BMI	LFSHF	GO IF LEFT
204	CA	LOOP	DEX		DECREMENT COUNT
205	30 2B		BMI	DONE	GO IF DONE
207	A0 00		LDY	#0	SETUP CARRY FLAG
209	46 YY		LSR	LSDP	SET CARRY WITH LSB
20B	90 01		BCC	NOC1	GO IF NO CARRY
20D	C8		INY		CARRY
20E	46 XX	NOC1	LSR	MSDP	SHIFT MS BYTE
210	90 06		BCC	NOC2	GO IF NO CARRY
212	A5 YY		LDA	LSDP	GET LS BYTE
214	09 80		ORA	#$80	
216	85 YY		STA	LSDP	SET MSB
218	C0 00	NOC2	CPY	#0	TEST FOR CARRY FLAG
21A	F0 E8		BEQ	LOOP	GO IF NO CARRY
21C	A5 XX		LDA	MSDP	
21E	09 80		ORA	#$80	SET MSB OF MS BYTE
220	85 XX		STA	MSDP	
222	30 E0		BMI	LOOP	CONTINUE (JMP)
224	CA	LFSHF	DEX		INITIAL ADJUST
225	E8	LOP1	INX		INCREMENT COUNT
226	F0 0A		BEQ	DONE	GO IF DONE
228	A5 YY		LDA	LSDP	GET LS BYTE
22A	2A		ROL	A	SET OR RESET CARRY
22B	26 XX		ROL	MSDP	
22D	26 YY		ROL	LSDP	ROTATE
22F	4C 25 02		JMP	LOP1	CONTINUE
232	60	DONE	RTS		RETURN

TIME 8080

I. *Name:* TIME   Timing Loop for 8080
II. *Description:* Provides a variable time delay.
III. *Calling Sequence:* (B) = Timing count 1 to 255
           CALL   TIME
           (Return after time)
IV. *Volatility:* All registers returned with original contents except B.
V. *Notes:* With VALUE set to decimal 105, the increment per timing count is approximately 1 millisecond. The timing loop will then be 1 millisecond to 0.255 second. VALUE can be adjusted for longer time delays by using the following formula:
Time = (B) $\times$ 9.5 $\times$ VALUE for time in microseconds
The above assumes a 2-MHz clock on the microcomputer with no memory waits.

Loc	Contents	Label	Operand	Arguments	Comments
000	365	TIME	PUSH	PSW	SAVE A
001	325		PUSH	D	SAVE D
002	004		INR	B	ADJUST
003	257		XRA	A	CLEAR A FOR COMPARE
004	005	TIME1	DCR	B	DECREMENT TIME COUNT
005	312 022 000		JZ	DONE	GO IF DONE
010	021 012 000		LXI	D,VALUE	SETUP INNER LOOP
013	033	LOOP	DCX	D	DECREMENT 16 BITS
014	273				
015					
020	272		CMP	D	COMPARE TO 0
021	312 003 000		JZ	TIME1	GO IF INNER LOOP DONE
024	303 012 000		JMP	LOOP	NOT DONE
027	321	DONE	POP	D	RESTORE D
030	361		POP	PSW	RESTORE A
031	311		RET		
		VALUE	EQU	10	DECIMAL 10

TIME 6800

I. *Name:* TIME   Timing Loop for 6800
II. *Description:* Provides a variable time delay.
III. *Calling Sequence:* (A) = Timing count 1 to 255
                        JSR   TIME
                        (Return after time)
IV. *Volatility:* All registers returned with original contents except A.
V. *Notes:* With VALUE set to decimal 66, the increment per timing count is approximately 1 millisecond. The timing loop will then be 1 milliseconds to 0.255 second. VALUE can be adjusted for longer time delays by using the following approximate formula:

   Time = (A) × 80 × VALUE for time in microseconds.
   The above assumes a 1-MHz clock on the microcomputer with no memory waits.

Loc	Contents	Label	Operand	Arguments	Comments
100	FF 01 17	TIME	STX	SAVEX	SAVE INDEX
103	4C		INCA		ADJUST
104	4A	LOP1	DECA		COUNT — 1
105	27 0C		BEQ	DONE	GO IF DONE
107	CE 00 0A		LDX	#VALUE	
10A	8C 00 00	LOOP	CPX	#0	TEST FOR 0
10D	27 F5		BEQ	LOP1	GO IF DONE
10F	09		DEX		DECR INNER LOOP CNT
110	7E 01 0A		JMP	LOOP	
113	FE 01 17	DONE	LDX	SAVEX	RESTORE INDEX
116	39		RTS		RETURN
117		SAVEX	RMB	2	
		VALUE	EQU	70	

TIME 6502

I. *Name:* TIME   Timing Loop for 6502

II. *Description:* Provides a variable time delay.

III. *Calling Sequence:* (A) = Timing count 1 to 255
                           JSR   TIME
                           (Return after time)

IV. *Volatility:* All registers used.

V. *Notes:* With CNT1 and CNT2 set to 11 and 30, the increment per timing count is approximately 1 millisecond. The timing loop will then be 1 millisecond to 0.255 second. CNT1 and CNT2 can be adjusted for other time delays by using the following approximate formula for larger values of CNT1 and CNT2:

$$Time = 10 \times COUNT \times CNT1 \times CNT2$$
for time in microseconds

The above assumes a 1-MHz clock on the microcomputer with no memory waits.

Loc	Contents	Label	Operand	Arguments	Comments
200	A0 1E	TIME	LDY	#CNT2	SETUP SECOND LOOP
202	A2 0B	LOOP2	LDX	#CNT1	SETUP THIRD LOOP
204	CA	LOOP1	DEX		INNERMOST LOOP
205	D0 FD		BNE	LOOP1	GO IF NOT DONE
207	88		DEY		DECREMENT NEXT CNT
208	D0 F8		BNE	LOOP2	
20A	18		CLC		CLEAR C FOR ADD
20B	69 FF		ADC	#−1	DECREMENT OUTER CNT
20D	D0 F1		BNE	TIME	GO IF NOT DONE
20F	60		RTS		RETURN
		CNT1	EQU	11	
		CNT2	EQU	30	

UNSPM 8080

I. *Name:* UNSPM   Unsigned Single-Precision Multiply for 8080

II. *Description:* This subroutine multiplies a 16-bit unsigned number in D,E by an 8-bit unsigned number in A. The product returns in H,L. Reentrant.

III. *Calling Sequence:* (D,E) = Multiplicand

(A) = Multiplier

CALL   UNSPM

[Return with (H,L) = Product]

IV. *Volatility:* All registers returned with original values except H,L, and B.

V. *Notes:* No check is made on overflow condition. May be used as a single-precision multiply with (D) = 0 and sp operand in E.

A signed multiply can be implemented by taking absolute values of the operands, calling this subroutine, and then converting the product to the proper sign.

Loc	Contents	Label	Operand	Arguments	Comments
000	041 000 000	UNSPM	LXI	H,0	CLEAR PRODUCT
003	006 010		MVI	B,8	SETUP COUNT
005	051	LOOP	DAD	H	SHIFT PARTIAL PRODUCT
006	007		RLC		ROTATE M'IER BIT
007	322 013 000		JNC	NOC	GO IF NOT 1
012	031		DAD	D	1 — ADD M'CAND
013	005	NOC	DCR	B	DECREMENT COUNT
014	302 005 000		JNZ	LOOP	CONTINUE
017	311		RET		RETURN

UNSPM 6800

I. *Name:* UNSPM   Unsigned Single-Precision Multiply for 6800
II. *Description:* This subroutine multiplies a 16-bit unsigned number in MCAND,MCAND+1 by an 8-bit unsigned number in the A accumulator. The product returns in RES,RES+1. Not reentrant.
III. *Calling Sequence:* (MCAND,MCAND+1) = Multiplicand
   (A) = Multiplier
   JSR   UNSPM
   [Return with (RES,RES+1) = Product]
IV. *Volatility:* All registers used. Multiplier destroyed. Multiplicand preserved.
V. *Notes:* No check is made on overflow condition. May be used as a single-precision multiply with MCAND = 0 and MCAND+1 = sp operand.

A signed multiply can be implemented by taking absolute values of the operands, calling this subroutine, and then converting the product to the proper sign.

Loc	Contents	Label	Operand	Arguments	Comments
100	CE 00 08	UNSPM	LDX	#8	SETUP INDEX
103	5F		CLRB		
104	D7 XX		STAB	RES	CLEAR RESULT
106	D7 YY		STAB	RES+1	
108	78 00 YY	LOOP	ASL	RES+1	SHIFT PARTIAL PRODUCT
10B	79 00 XX		ROL	RES	
10E	48		ASLA		SHIFT OUT M'IER BIT
10F	24 0C		BCC	NOC	GO IF NO CARRY
111	D6 ZZ		LDAB	MCAND+1	GET M'CAND LS
113	DB YY		ADDB	RES+1	ADD RES LS
115	D7 YY		STAB	RES+1	FIND PARTIAL PROD
117	D6 WW		LDAB	MCAND	GET M'CAND MS
119	D9 XX		ADCB	RES	ADD RES MS
11B	D7 XX		STAB	RES	FIND PARTIAL PROD
11D	09	NOC	DEX		DECREMENT COUNT
11E	26 E8		BNE	LOOP	CONTINUE
120	39		RTS		RETURN FROM SUBR

UNSPM 6502

I. *Name:* UNSPM Unsigned Single-Precision Multiply for 6502
II. *Description:* See UNSPM 6800.
III. *Calling Sequence:* See UNSPM 6800.
IV. *Volatility:* All registers used.
V. *Notes:* See UNSPM 6800.

Loc	Contents	Label	Operand	Arguments	Comments
200	48	UNSPM	PHA		SAVE M'IER
201	A9 00		LDA	#0	ZERO RESULT
203	85 XX		STA	RES	
205	85 YY		STA	RES+1	
207	68		PLA		RESTORE M'IER
208	A2 08		LDX	#8	SETUP COUNT
20A	18	LOOP	CLC		
20B	26 YY		ROL	RES+1	SHIFT PARTIAL PRODUCT
20D	26 XX		ROL	RES	
20F	0A		ASL	A	SHIFT OUT M'IER BIT
210	90 0F		BCC	NOC1	GO IF NO CARRY
212	A8		TAY		SAVE M'IER
213	A5 YY		LDA	RES+1	GET RESULT LS
215	18		CLC		FOR ADD
216	65 WW		ADC	MCAND+1	GET RESULT LS
218	85 YY		STA	RES+1	
21A	A5 XX		LDA	RES	GET RESULT MS
21C	65 VV		ADC	MCAND	ADD MCAND MS
21E	85 XX		STA	RES	NEW RESULT MS
220	98		TYA		RESTORE M'IER
221	CA	NOC1	DEX		DECREMENT COUNT
222	D0 E6		BNE	LOOP	GO IF NOT DONE
224	60		RTS		RETURN

UNSPD 8080

I. *Name:* UNSPD   Unsigned Single-Precision Divide for 8080

II. *Description:* This subroutine divides a 16-bit unsigned number in H,L by an 8-bit unsigned number in B. The quotient returns in H,L and the remainder returns in A. Reentrant.

III. *Calling Sequence:* (H,L) = Dividend
   (B) = Divisor
   JSR   UNSPD
   [Return with (H,L) = Quotient, (A) = remainder]

IV. *Volatility:* All registers returned with original values except A and H,L.

V. *Notes:* No check is made on division by zero. May be used as a single-precision divide by clearing H and putting dividend in L.

Loc	Contents	Label	Operand	Arguments	Comments
000	305	UNSPD	PUSH	B	SAVE B,C
001	257		XRA	A	CLEAR A FOR REMAINDER
002	016 021		MVI	C,17	SETUP COUNT
004	303 014 000		JMP	START	
007	220	LOOP	SUB	B	A − B
010	362 021 000		JP	NREST	GO IF NO RESTORE
013	200		ADD	B	RESTORE
014	051	START	DAD	H	SHIFT H,L LEFT
015	027		RAL		ZERO TO Q
016	303 024 000		JMP	CONT	CONTINUE
021	051	NREST	DAD	H	SHIFT H,L LEFT
022	027		RAL		INTO A
023	043		INX	H	ONE FOR Q
024	015	CONT	DCR	C	DECREMENT COUNT
025	302 007 000		JNZ	LOOP	GO IF NOT DONE
030	037		RAR		RESTORE REMAINDER
031	301		POP	B	RESTORE B,C
032	311		RET		RETURN

UNSPD 6800

I. *Name:* UNSPD   Unsigned Single-Precision Divide for 6800

II. *Description:* This subroutine divides a 16-bit unsigned number in (DVDN, DVDN+1) by an 8-bit unsigned number in (DVSR). The quotient returns in DVDN, DVDN+1 and the remainder returns in RMNDR.

III. *Calling Sequence:* (DVDN,DVDN+1) = Dividend
   (DVSR) = Divisor
   JSR   UNSPD
   [Return with (DVDN,DVDN+1) = quotient, (RMNDR) = remainder]

IV. *Volatility:* The B accumulator is not used.

V. *Notes:* No check is made on division by zero. May be used as a single-precision divide by clearing DVDN and putting dividend in DVDN+1.

Loc	Contents	Label	Operand	Arguments	Comments
100	7F 00 XX	UNSPD	CLR	RMNDR	CLEAR REMAINDER
103	CE 00 11		LDX	#17	SETUP COUNT
106	20 06		BRA	START	START
108	96 XX	LOOP	LDAA	RMNDR	GET CURRENT MS BYTE
10A	90 WW		SUBA	DVSR	SUBTRACT
10C	2A 03		BPL	NREST	GO IF NO RESTORE
10E	0C	START	CLC		CLEAR CARRY
10F	20 03		BRA	MERGQ	GO TO SET Q
111	97 XX	NREST	STAA	RMNDR	NEW PARTIAL Q
113	0D		SEC		SET C FOR Q=1
114	79 00 ZZ	MERGQ	ROL	DVDN+1	MERGE Q
117	79 00 YY		ROL	DVDN	
11A	09		DEX		DECREMENT COUNT
11B	27 05		BEQ	RTN	GO IF DONE
11D	79 XX		ROL	RMNDR	SHIFT BIT
120	26 E6		BRA	LOOP	CONTINUE
122	39	RTN	RTS		RETURN

UNSPD 6502

I. *Name:* UNSPD Unsigned Single-Precision Divide for 6502
II. *Description:* See UNSPD 6800.
III. *Calling Sequence:* See UNSPD 6800.
IV. *Volatility:* Y register not used and returned with original contents.
V. *Notes:* See UNSPD 6800.

Loc	Contents	Label	Operand	Arguments	Comments
200	A9 00	UNSPD	LDA	#0	ZERO REMAINDER
202	85 XX		STA	RMNDR	
204	A2 11		LDX	#17	SETUP COUNT
206	4C 10 02		JMP	START	START
209	A5 XX	LOOP	LDA	RMNDR	GET CURRENT RESIDUE
20B	38		SEC		SET C FOR SUB
20C	E5 WW		SBC	DVSR	
20E	10 04		BPL	NREST	GO IF NO RESTORE
210	18	START	CLC		Q=0
211	4C 17 02		JMP	MERGQ	GO TO SET Q
214	85 XX	NREST	STA	RMNDR	NEW RESIDUE
216	38		SEC		Q=1
217	26 ZZ	MERGQ	ROL	DVDN+1	
219	26 YY		ROL	DVDN	
21B	CA		DEX		DECREMENT COUNT
21C	F0 05		BEQ	RTN	GO IF DONE
21E	26 XX		ROL	RMNDR	SHIFT LEFT
220	4C 09 02		JMP	LOOP	CONTINUE
223	60	RTN	RTS		RETURN

MPADD 8080

I. *Name:* MPADD   Multiple-Precision Add for 8080

II. *Description:* This subroutine adds two N-precision numbers. From single- to 127-byte precision can be used. Both operands are in memory. The destination operand is added to the source operand and the N-precision result replaces the destination operand. Reentrant.

III. *Calling Sequence:* (C) = Precision, 1 to N
   (D,E) = Start of source operand
   (H,L) = Start of destination operand
   CALL   MPADD
   (Return with result in destination operand)

IV. *Volatility:* All registers returned with original values.

V. *Notes:* No check is made on overflow.

Loc	Contents	Label	Operand	Arguments	Comments
000	305	MPADD	PUSH	B	SAVE B,C
001	006 000		MVI	B,0	SETUP FOR ADD
003	011		DAD	B	POINT TO LAST BYTE+1
004	353		XCHG		SWAP
005	011		DAD	B	LAST BYTE OF SRCE+1
006	353		XCHG		SWAP BACK
007	067		STC		
010	077		CMC		CLEAR CARRY
011	015	LOOP	DCR	C	DECREMENT COUNT
012	372 025 000		JM	DONE	GO IF DONE
015	033		DCX	D	GO TO NEXT HIGHER ORDER
016	053		DCX	H	
017	032		LDAX	D	GET SOURCE
020	216		ADC	M	ADD DEST + C
021	167		MOV	M,A	REPLACE DEST BYTE
022	303 011 000		JMP	LOOP	
025	301	DONE	POP	B	RESTORE B,C
026	311		RET		RETURN

MPADD 6800

I. *Name:* MPADD Multiple-Precision Add for 6800
II. *Description:* See MPADD 8080.
III. *Calling Sequence:* (A) = Precision, 1 to N
                        (SRCE) = Start of source operand
                        (DEST) = Start of destination operand
                        JSR   MPADD
                        (Return with result in destination operand)
IV. *Volatility:* B accumulator restored to original value.
V. *Notes:* No check is made on overflow.

Loc	Contents	Label	Operand	Arguments	Comments
100	37	MPADD	PSHB		SAVE B
101	0C		CLC		CLEAR CARRY FIRST TIME
102	4A	LOOP	DECA		
103	2B 15		BMI	DONE	GO IF DONE
105	B7 01 11		STAA	INST1 + 1	MODIFY DISPLACEMENTS
108	B7 01 15		STAA	INST2 + 1	
10B	B7 01 17		STAA	INST3 + 1	
10E	DE XX		LDX	SRCE	GET SOURCE PNTR
110	E6 00	INST1	LDAB	X	GET SOURCE BYTE
112	DE YY		LDX	DEST	GET DEST PNTR
114	E9 00	INST2	ADCB	X	SOURCE + DEST
116	E7 00	INST3	STAB	X	STORE IN DEST
118	20 E8		BRA	LOOP	CONTINUE
11A	33	DONE	PULB		RESTORE B
11B	39		RTS		RETURN

MPADD 6502

I. *Name:* MPADD   Multiple-Precision Add for 6502

II. *Description:* This subroutine adds two N-precision numbers. From single- to 127-byte precision can be used. Both operands are in memory. The destination operand is added to the source operand and the N-precision result replaces the destination operand.

III. *Calling Sequence:* (X) = Precision, 1 through N
   (SRCE) = Start of source operand
   (DEST) = Start of destination operand
   JSR   MPADD
   (Return with result in destination operand)

IV. *Volatility:* All registers used.

V. *Notes:* Locations SRCE and DEST are assumed in page 0 specifying 16-bit addresses (LS byte followed by MS byte).

Loc	Contents	Label	Operand	Arguments	Comments
200	8A	MPADD	TXA		X TO Y FOR ACCESS
201	A8		TAY		
202	88		DEY		POINT TO LAST BYTE
203	18		CLC		CLEAR C FOR ADD
204	CA	LOOP	DEX		DECREMENT COUNT
205	30 0A		BMI	DONE	GO IF DONE
207	B1 XX		LDA	(SRCE),Y	GET SOURCE BYTE
209	71 YY		ADC	(DEST),Y	ADD DEST BYTE
20B	91 YY		STA	(DEST),Y	SAVE RESULT
20D	88		DEY		POINT TO HIGHER ORDER
20E	4C 04 02		JMP	LOOP	CONTINUE
211	60	DONE	RTS		RETURN

MPSUB 8080

I. *Name:* MPSUB   Multiple-Precision Subtract for 8080

II. *Description:* This subroutine subtracts two *N*-precision numbers. From single- to 127-byte precision can be used. Both operands are in memory. The destination operand is subtracted from the source operand and the *N*-precision result replaces the destination operand. Reentrant.

III. *Calling Sequence:* (C) = Precision, 1 to *N*
                              (D,E) = Start of source operand
                              (H,L) = Start of destination operand
                              CALL   MPSUB
                              (Return with result in destination operand)

IV. *Volatility:* All registers returned with original values.

V. *Notes:* No check is made on overflow.

Loc	Contents	Label	Operand	Arguments	Comments
000	305	MPADD	PUSH	B	SAVE B,C
001	006 000		MVI	B,0	SETUP FOR ADD
003	011		DAD	B	POINT TO LAST BYTE+1
004	353		XCHG		SWAP
005	011		DAD	B	LAST BYTE OF SRCE+1
006	353		XCHG		SWAP BACK
007	067		STC		
010	077		CMC		CLEAR CARRY
011	015	LOOP	DCR	C	DECREMENT COUNT
012	372 025 000		JM	DONE	GO IF DONE
015	033		DCX	D	GO TO NEXT HIGHER
016	053		DCX	H	ORDER
017	032		LDAX	D	GET SOURCE
020	236		SBB	M	SOURCE - DEST - B
021	167		MOV	M,A	REPLACE DEST BYTE
022	303 011 000		JMP	LOOP	
025	301	DONE	POP	B	RESTORE B,C
026	311		RET		RETURN

MPSUB 6800

I. *Name:* MPSUB   Multiple-Precision Subtract for 6800
II. *Description:* See MPSUB 8080.
III. *Calling Sequence:* (A) = Precision, 1 to N
    (SRCE) = Start of source operand
    (DEST) = Start of destination operand
    JSR   MPSUB
    (Return with result in destination operand)
IV. *Volatility:* B accumulator restored to original value.
V. *Notes:* No check is made on overflow.

Loc	Contents	Label	Operand	Arguments	Comments
100	37	MPADD	PSHB		SAVE B
101	0C		CLC		CLEAR CARRY FIRST TIME
102	4A	LOOP	DECA		
103	2B 15		BMI	DONE	GO IF DONE
105	B7 01 11		STAA	INST1+1	MODIFY DISPLACEMENTS
108	B7 01 15		STAA	INST2+1	
10B	B7 01 17		STAA	INST3+1	
10E	DE XX		LDX	SRCE	GET SOURCE PNTR
110	E6 00	INST1	LDAB	X	GET SOURCE BYTE
112	DE YY		LDX	DEST	GET DEST PNTR
114	E2 00	INST2	SBCB	X	SOURCE-DEST
116	E7 00	INST3	STAB	X	STORE IN DEST
118	20 E8		BRA	LOOP	CONTINUE
11A	33	DONE	PULB		RESTORE B
11B	39		RTS		RETURN

MPSUB 6502

I. *Name:* MPSUB   Multiple-Precision Subtract for 6502
II. *Description:* This subroutine subtracts two *N*-precision numbers. From single- to 127-byte precision can be used. Both operands are in memory. The destination operand is subtracted from the source operand and the *N*-precision result replaces the destination operand.
III. *Calling Sequence:* See MPADD 6502.
IV. *Volatility:* All registers used.
V. *Notes:* Locations SRCE and DEST assumed in page 0 specifying 16-bit addresses (LS byte followed by MS byte).

Loc	Contents	Label	Operand	Arguments	Comments
200	8A	MPSUB	TXA		X TO Y FOR ACCESS
201	A8		TAY		
202	88		DEY		POINT TO LAST BYTE
203	38		SEC		SET C FOR SUB
204	CA	LOOP	DEX		DECREMENT COUNT
205	30 0A		BMI	DONE	GO IF DONE
207	B1 XX		LDA	(SRCE),Y	GET SOURCE BYTE
209	F1 YY		SBC	(DEST),Y	SUB DEST BYTE
20B	91 YY		STA	(DEST),Y	SAVE RESULT
20D	88		DEY		POINT TO HIGHER ORDER
20E	4C 04 02		JMP	LOOP	CONTINUE
211	60	DONE	RTS		RETURN

ASBXB 8080

I. *Name:* ASBXB   ASCII Binary to Binary Subroutine for 8080
II. *Description:* This subroutine converts an 8-character ASCII string, assumed to be ASCII zeros and ones, to an 8-bit binary value. Reentrant.
III. *Calling Sequence:* (H,L) = Address of start of string
  CALL   ASBXB
  [Return with (B) = binary value]
IV. *Volatility:* All registers returned with original values except B and H,L. (H,L) points to last ASCII character plus one.
V. *Notes:* Continuing calls may be made to ASBXB with returned value in H,L to convert a longer string of binary values.

Loc	Contents	Label	Operand	Arguments	Comments
000	365	ASBXB	PUSH	PSW	SAVE A
001	325		PUSH	D	SAVE D
002	006 000		MVI	B,0	ZERO RESULT
004	026 011		MVI	D,9	INITIALIZE COUNT
006	025	LOOP	DCR	D	DECREMENT INDEX
007	312 027 000		JZ	DONE	GO IF DONE
012	176		MOV	A,M	GET NEXT CHARACTER
013	346 177		ANI	0177	GET SEVEN BITS
015	326 060		SUI	060	CONVERT TO BINARY
017	037		RAR		SET CARRY
020	170		MOV	A,B	GET PARTIAL RESULT
021	027		RAL		MERGE CARRY
022	107		MOV	B,A	
023	043		INX	H	POINT TO NEXT
024	303 006 000		JMP	LOOP	CONTINUE
027	321	DONE	POP	D	RESTORE D
030	361		POP	PSW	RESTORE A
031	311		RET		RETURN

ASBXB 6800

I. *Name:* ASBXB   ASCII Binary to Binary Subroutine for 6800

II. *Description:* This subroutine converts an 8-character ASCII string, assumed to be ASCII zeros and ones, to an 8-bit binary value. Reentrant.

III. *Calling Sequence:* (X) = Address of start of string
     JSR   ASBXB
     [Return with (A) = binary value]

IV. *Volatility:* B register restored with original contents. X register points to last ASCII character plus one.

V. *Notes:* Continuing calls may be made to ASBXB with returned pointer in X to convert a longer string of binary values.

Loc	Contents	Label	Operand	Arguments	Comments
100	37	ASBXB	PSHB		SAVE B
101	86 08		LDAA	#8	INDEX COUNT
103	36		PSHA		SAVE
104	4F		CLRA		CLEAR RESULT
105	E6 00	LOOP	LDAB	X	GET NEXT ASCII CHAR
107	C4 7F		ANDB	#$7F	GET SEVEN BITS
109	C0 30		SUBB	#$30	CONVERT TO 0 OR 1
10B	1B		ABA		MERGE INTO RESULT
10C	08		INX		BUMP POINTER
10D	33		PULB		GET COUNT
10E	5A		DECB		DECREMENT
10F	27 04		BEQ	DONE	GO IF DONE
111	37		PSHB		SAVE COUNT
112	48		ASLA		SHIFT FOR NEXT BIT
113	20 F0		BRA	LOOP	
115	33	DONE	PULB		RESTORE B
116	39		RTS		RETURN

ASBXB 6502

I. *Name:* ASBXB   ASCII Binary to Binary Subroutine for 6502

II. *Description:* This subroutine converts an 8-character ASCII string, assumed to be ASCII zeros and ones to an 8-bit binary value.

III. *Calling Sequence:* (DEST) = Address of start of string
    JSR   ASBXB
    [Return with (A) = binary value]

IV. *Volatility:* All registers used.

V. *Notes:* Continuing calls may be made to ASBXB with returned pointer in DEST to convert a longer string of binary values. DEST assumed to be in page 0 and specifying a 16-bit address (LS byte followed by MS byte).

Loc	Contents	Label	Operand	Arguments	Comments
200	A9 00	ASBXB	LDA	#0	CLEAR RESULT
202	48		PHA		SAVE
203	A2 08		LDX	#8	INITIALIZE COUNT
205	A0 00		LDY	#0	INITIALIZE INDEX
207	B1 XX	LOOP	LDA	(DEST),Y	GET ASCII BYTE
209	29 7F		AND	#7F	GET SEVEN BITS
20B	18		CLC		
20C	E9 30		SBC	#$30	CONVERT TO BINARY
20E	68		PLA		GET RESULT
20F	69 00		ADC	#0	MERGE CARRY
211	CA		DEX		DECREMENT COUNT
212	F0 06		BEQ	DONE	GO IF DONE
214	0A		ASL		SHIFT
215	48		PHA		SAVE
216	C8		INY		POINT TO NEXT CHAR
217	4C 07 02		JMP	LOOP	CONTINUE
21A	48	DONE	PHA		
21B	A5 XX		LDA	DEST	GET LS ADDRESS
21D	18		CLC		
21E	69 08		ADC	#8	POINT TO NEXT
220	85 XX		STA	DEST	
222	90 02		BCC	NOC	GO IF NO CARRY
224	E6 YY		INC	DEST+1	BUMP MS ADDRESS
226	68	NOC	PLA		RESTORE RESULT
227	60		RTS		RETURN

ASDXB 8080

I. *Name:* ASDXB   ASCII Decimal to Binary Subroutine for 8080

II. *Description:* This subroutine converts a five-character ASCII string, assumed to be ASCII decimal digits, to a 16-bit binary value. Reentrant.

                  [Return with (D,E) = value]

III. *Calling Sequence:* (H,L) = Address of start of string

                  CALL   ASDXB

IV. *Volatility:* All registers returned with original values except D,E and H,L. (H,L) points to last ASCII character plus one.

V. *Notes:* Continuing calls may be made to ASDXB with returned pointer in H,L to convert a longer string of decimal values. Conversion of single-precision values is accomplished by padding the first two characters of the string with blanks and obtaining an 8-bit value in C.

Conversion of negated values may be handled by bypassing any sign character, converting, and then adjusting for sign.

Loc	Contents	Label	Operand	Arguments	Comments
000	365	ASDXB	PUSH	PSW	SAVE A
001	305		PUSH	B	SAVE B,C
002	026 005		MVI	D,5	
004	325		PUSH	D	INITIALIZE INDEX
005	021 000 000		LXI	D,0	INITIALIZE RESULT
010	176	LOOP	MOV	A,M	GET CHARACTER
011	346 177		ANI	0177	GET SEVEN BITS
013	326 060		SUI	060	CONVERT TO BCD
015	203		ADD	E	MERGE IN RESULT
016	322 022 000		JNC	NOC	GO IF NO CARRY
021	024		INR	D	CARRY TO MSB
022	137	NOC	MOV	E,A	SAVE IN D,E
023	301		POP	B	GET INDEX
024	005		DCR	B	DECREMENT COUNT
025	312 045 000		JZ	DONE	GO IF DONE
030	305		PUSH	B	NOT DONE
031	353		XCHG		SWAP
032	051		DAD	H	TIMES 2
033	345		PUSH	H	SAVE
034	051		DAD	H	TIMES 4
035	051		DAD	H	TIMES 8
036	301		POP	B	GET TIMES 2
037	011		DAD	B	NOW TIMES 10
040	353		XCHG		
041	043		INX	H	POINT TO NEXT CHAR
042	303 010 000		JMP	LOOP	CONTINUE
045	043	DONE	INX	H	POINT TO LAST+1
046	301		POP	B	RESTORE B,C
047	361		POP	PSW	RESTORE A
050	311		RET		RETURN

ASDXB 6800

I. *Name:* ASDXB   ASCII Decimal to Binary Subroutine for 6800
II. *Description:* This subroutine converts a five-character ASCII string, assumed to be ASCII decimal digits, to a 16-bit binary value.
III. *Calling Sequence:* (X) = Address of start of string
    JSR   ASDXB
    [Return with (A,B) = result]
IV. *Volatility:* All registers used.
V. *Notes:* See ASDXB 8080. Pointer in X.

Loc	Contents	Label	Operand	Arguments	Comments
100	7F 00 XX	ASDXB	CLR	MCAND	
103	7F 00 YY		CLR	MCAND+1	CLEAR M'CAND
106	C6 04		LDAB	#4	INITIALIZE COUNT
108	A6 00	LOOP	LDAA	X	GET CHAR
10A	84 7F		ANDA	#$7F	GET SEVEN BITS
10C	80 30		SUBA	#$30	CONVERT TO BCD
10E	9B YY		ADDA	MCAND+1	
110	97 YY		STAA	MCAND+1	ADD TO PARTIAL RESULT
112	24 03		BCC	NOC	GO IF NO CARRY
114	7C 00 XX		INC	MCAND	
117	5A	NOC	DECB		DECREMENT COUNT
118	2B 16		BMI	DONE	GO IF DONE
11A	37		PSHB		SAVE CNT
11B	DF ZZ		STX	TEMP1	SAVE INDEX
11D	86 0A		LDAA	#10	
11F	BD XX XX*		JSR	UNSPM	10 TIMES RESULT
122	96 UU		LDAA	RES	
124	97 XX		STAA	MCAND	
126	96 VV		LDAA	RES+1	
128	97 YY		STAA	MCAND+1	TRANSFER PRODUCT
12A	33		PULB		RESTORE B
12B	DE ZZ		LDX	TEMP1	RESTORE X
12D	08		INX		POINT TO LOWER ORDER
12E	20 D8		BRA	LOOP	CONTINUE
130	08	DONE	INX		POINT TO LAST+1
131	96 XX		LDAA	MCAND	
133	D6 YY		LDAB	MCAND+1	GET RESULT
135	39		RTS		RETURN

ASDXB 6502

I. *Name:* ASDXB   ASCII Decimal to Binary Subroutine for 6502
II. *Description:* This subroutine converts a five-character ASCII string, assumed to be ASCII decimal digits, to a 16-bit binary value.
III. *Calling Sequence:* (DEST) = Address of start of string
   JSR   ASDXB
   [Return with (MCAND,MCAND+1) =
                                        result]
IV. *Volatility:* All registers used.
V. *Notes:* See ASDXB 8080. Pointer in DEST assumed to be page 0 specifying 16-bit address (LS byte followed by MS byte).

Loc	Contents	Label	Operand	Arguments	Comments
200	A9 00	ASDXB	LDA	#0	
202	85 XX		STA	MCAND	
204	85 YY		STA	MCAND+1	ZERO MCAND
206	A8		TAY		
207	B1 UU	LOOP	LDA	(DEST),Y	GET ASCII CHAR
209	29 7F		AND	#$7F	SEVEN BITS
20B	38		SEC		
20C	E9 30		SBC	#$30	CONVERT TO BCD
20E	18		CLC		
20F	65 YY		ADC	MCAND+1	
211	85 YY		STA	MCAND+1	ADD TO PARTIAL RESULT
213	90 02		BCC	NOC	GO IF NO CARRY
215	E6 XX		INC	MCAND	
217	C8	NOC	INY		
218	C0 05		CPY	#5	TEST FOR DONE
21A	F0 16		BEQ	DONE	GO IF DONE
21C	A9 0A		LDA	#10	
21E	8C 3E 02		STY	TEMP	SAVE Y
221	20 XX XX*		JSR	UNSPM	10 TIMES
224	AC 3E 02		LDY	TEMP	RESTORE Y
227	A5 SS		LDA	RES	
229	85 XX		STA	MCAND	
22B	A5 TT		LDA	RES+1	
22D	85 YY		STA	MCAND+1	TRANSFER PRODUCT
22F	4C 07 02		JMP	LOOP	
232	A5 UU	DONE	LDA	DEST	
234	18		CLC		
235	69 05		ADC	#5	
237	85 UU		STA	DEST	POINT TO LAST+1
239	90 02		BCC	NOC1	
23B	E6 VV		INC	DEST+1	BUMP MS ADDRESS
23D	60	NOC1	RTS		RETURN
23E		TEMP	RMB	1	

ASOXB 8080

I. *Name:* ASOXB   ASCII Octal to Binary Subroutine for 8080
II. *Description:* This subroutine converts a six-character ASCII string, assumed to be ASCII octal digits, to a 16-bit binary value. Reentrant.
III. *Calling Sequence:* (H,L) = Address of start of string
                       CALL ASOXB
                       [Return with (B,C) = value]
IV. *Volatility:* All registers returned with original values except B,C and H,L. (H,L) points to last ASCII character plus one.
V. *Notes:* Continuing calls may be made to ASOXB with returned value in H,L to convert a longer string of binary values. Conversion of single-precision values is accomplished by padding the first three characters of the string with blanks and obtaining an 8-bit value in C.

Loc	Contents	Label	Operand	Arguments	Comments
000	365	ASOXB	PUSH	PSW	SAVE A
001	325		PUSH	D	SAVE D
002	001 000 000		LXI	B,0	ZERO RESULT
005	026 006		MVI	D,6	INITIALIZE COUNT
007	176	LOOP	MOV	A,M	GET NEXT CHARACTER
010	346 177		ANI	0177	GET SEVEN BITS
012	326 060		SUI	060	CONVERT TO OCTAL
014	261		ORA	C	MERGE WITH PARTIAL RES
015	117		MOV	C,A	
016	043		INX	H	POINT TO NEXT CHAR
017	025		DCR	D	DECREMENT INDEX
020	312 037 000		JZ	DONE	GO IF DONE
023	345		PUSH	H	SAVE H,L
024	305		PUSH	B	TRANSFER B
025	341		POP	H	
026	051		DAD	H	
027	051		DAD	H	
030	051		DAD	H	SHIFT LEFT 3 BITS
031	345		PUSH	H	TRANSFER TO B
032	301		POP	B	
033	341		POP	H	RESTORE POINTER
034	303 007 000		JMP	LOOP	
037	321	DONE	POP	D	RESTORE D,E
040	361		POP	PSW	RESTORE A
041	311		RET		

ASHXB 8080

I. *Name:* ASHXB   ASCII Hexadecimal to Binary Subroutine for 8080
II. *Description:* This subroutine converts a two-character ASCII string, assumed to be ASCII hexadecimal digits, to an 8-bit binary value. Reentrant.
III. *Calling Sequence:* (H,L) = Address of start of string
    CALL   ASHXB
    [Return with (B) = value]
IV. *Volatility:* All registers returned with original values except B and H,L. (H,L) points to last ASCII character plus one.
V. *Notes:* Continuing calls may be made to ASHXB with returned pointer in H,L to convert a longer string of hexadecimal values.

Loc	Contents	Label	Operand	Arguments	Comments
000	365	ASHXB	PUSH	PSW	SAVE A
001	176		MOV	A,M	GET FIRST CHARACTER
002	315 024 000		CALL	CONVT	CONVERT TO HEX
005	207		ADD	A	
006	207		ADD	A	
007	207		ADD	A	
010	207		ADD	A	SHIFT TO MS 4 BITS
011	107		MOV	B,A	SAVE IN B
012	043		INX	H	POINT TO NEXT CHAR
013	176		MOV	A,M	GET NEXT CHAR
014	315 024 000		CALL	CONVT	CONVERT TO HEX
017	260		ORA	B	MERGE FIRST
020	107		MOV	B,A	RETURN IN B
021	043		INX	H	BUMP FOR RETURN
022	361		POP	PSW	RESTORE A
023	311		RET		RETURN
024	346 177	CONVT	ANI	0177	GET SEVEN BITS
026	326 060		SUI	060	START CONVERT
030	376 012		CPI	10	TEST FOR ALPHA
032	372 037 000		JM	CONT	GO IF 0 — 9
035	326 007		SUI	7	CONVERT A — F
037	311	CONT	RET		RETURN TO ASHXB

ASHXB 6800

I. *Name:* ASHXB   ASCII Hexadecimal to Binary Subroutine for 6800
II. *Description:* See ASHXB 8080. Reentrant.
III. *Calling Sequence:* (X) = Address of start of string
  JSR   ASHXB
  [Return with (A) = value]
IV. *Volatility:* B accumulator not used. X register points to last ASCII character plus one.
V. *Notes:* Continuing calls may be made to ASHXB with returned pointer in X to convert a longer string of hexadecimal values.

Loc	Contents	Label	Operand	Arguments	Comments
100	37	ASBXB	PSHB		SAVE B
101	A6 00		LDAA	X	GET FIRST ASCII CHAR
103	8D 0E		BSR	CVERT	CONVERT TO BINARY
105	16		TAB		SAVE
106	08		INX		POINT TO NEXT CHAR
107	A6 00		LDAA	X	GET NEXT ASCII CHAR
109	8D 08		BSR	CVERT	CONVERT TO BINARY
10B	58		ASLB		
10C	58		ASLB		
10D	58		ASLB		
10E	58		ASLB		ALIGN SECOND DIGIT
10F	1B		ABA		MERGE
110	08		INX		POINT TO NEXT FOR RTN
111	33		PULB		RESTORE B
112	39		RTS		RETURN
113	84 7F	CVERT	ANDA	#$7F	GET SEVEN BITS
115	80 30		SUBA	#$30	FIND DISPLACEMENT
117	81 0A		CMPA	#10	TEST FOR 0 — 9
119	2B 02		BMI	NAD	GO IF 0 — 9
11B	80 07		SUBA	#7	ADJUST FOR A — F
11D	39	NAD	RTS		

ASHXB 6502

I. *Name:* ASHXB ASCII Hexadecimal to Binary Subroutine for 6502

II. *Description:* See ASHXB 8080.

III. *Calling Sequence:* (DEST) = Address of start of string
    JSR ASHXB
    [Return with (A) = value]

IV. *Volatility:* X register not used.

V. *Notes:* On return (DEST) holds address of last character stored plus one. Continuing calls may be made to ASHXB with returned pointer in DEST to convert a string of hexadecimal values. DEST assumed to be a page 0 location specifying a 16-bit address (LS byte followed by MS byte).

Loc	Contents	Label	Operand	Arguments	Comments
200	A0 01	ASHXB	LDY	#1	POINT TO SECOND DIGIT
202	B1 XX		LDA	(DEST),Y	GET CHARACTER
204	20 25 02		JSR	CVERT	CONVERT TO HEX DIGIT
207	48		PHA		SAVE
208	88		DEY		
209	B1 XX		LDA	(DEST),Y	GET SECOND CHARACTER
20B	20 25 02		JSR	CVERT	CONVERT
20E	0A		ASL		
20F	0A		ASL		
210	0A		ASL		
211	0A		ASL		ALIGN TO MS POSITION
212	85 ZZ		STA	TEMP1	
214	68		PLA		GET SECOND DIGIT
215	05 ZZ		ORA	TEMP1	MERGE DIGITS
217	48		PHA		SAVE
218	A5 XX		LDA	DEST	GET POINTER
21A	18		CLC		CLEAR FOR ADD
21B	69 02		ADC	#2	POINT TO LAST+1
21D	85 XX		STA	DEST	
21F	90 02		BCC	NOC	GO IF NO CARRY
221	E6 YY		INC	DEST+1	BUMP MS ADDRESS
223	68	NOC	PLA		GET VALUE
224	60		RTS		RETURN
225	38	CVERT	SEC		SET FOR SUBTRACT
226	E9 30		SBC	#$30	
228	C9 0A		CMP	#10	TEST FOR 0—9
22A	30 02		BMI	NOAD	GO OF 0—9
22C	E9 07		SBC	#7	A—F
22E	60	NOAD	RTS		RETURN TO ASHXB

BXASB 8080

I. *Name:* BXASB Binary to ASCII Binary Subroutine for 8080

II. *Description:* This subroutine converts an 8-bit binary value to the equivalent ASCII digits and stores the ASCII characters in a specified 8-byte memory buffer. Reentrant.

III. *Calling Sequence:* (H,L) = Address of start of buffer
(B) = Value
CALL   BXASB
(Return with characters stored in buffer)

IV. *Volatility:* All registers returned with original values except H,L. (H,L) points to last ASCII character stored plus one.

V. *Notes:* Continuing calls may be made to BXASB with the returned pointer in H,L to convert additional binary values.

Loc	Contents	Label	Operand	Arguments	Comments
000	365	BXASB	PUSH	PSW	SAVE A
001	305		PUSH	B	SAVE B,C
002	016 011		MVI	C,9	SETUP INDEX
004	170		MOV	A,B	
005	015	LOOP	DCR	C	DECREMENT COUNT
006	312 025 000		JZ	DONE	GO IF DONE
011	006 060		MVI	B,060	ASCII 0
013	027		RAL		SHIFT OUT BIT
014	322 020 000		JNC	NOC	GO IF 0
017	004		INR	B	CHANGE TO 061
020	160	NOC	MOV	M,B	STORE CHARACTER
021	043		INX	H	BUMP POINTER
022	303 005 000		JMP	LOOP	
025	301	DONE	POP	B	RESTORE B,C
026	361		POP	PSW	RESTORE A
027	311		RET		

BXASB 6800

I. *Name:* BXASB   Binary to ASCII Binary Subroutine for 6800
II. *Description:* See BXASB 8080. Reentrant.
III. *Calling Sequence:* (X) = Address of start of buffer
                     (A) = Value
                     JSR   BXASB
                     (Return with characters stored in buffer)
IV. *Volatility:* B accumulator saved. X register points to last ASCII
           character stored plus one.
V. *Notes:* Continuing calls may be made to BXASB with the re-
           turned pointer in X to convert additional binary values.

Loc	Contents	Label	Operand	Arguments	Comments
100	37	BXASB	PSHB		SAVE B
101	C6 08		LDAB	#8	SETUP INDEX
103	37		PSHB		SAVE
104	C6 30	LOOP	LDAB	#$30	ASCII ZERO
106	49		ROLA		SHIFT BIT TO C
107	24 01		BCC	NAD	GO IF 0
109	5C		INCB		ASCII ONE
10A	E7 00	NAD	STAB	X	STORE CHARACTER
10C	08		INX		POINT TO NEXT
10D	33		PULB		GET INDEX COUNT
10E	5A		DECB		DECREMENT
10F	27 03		BEQ	DONE	GO IF DONE
111	37		PSHB		SAVE INDEX
112	20 F0		BRA	LOOP	CONTINUE
114	33	DONE	PULB		RESTORE B
115	39		RTS		RETURN

BXASB 6502

I. *Name:* BXASB   Binary to ASCII Binary Subroutine for 6502

II. *Description:* See BXASB 8800.

III. *Calling Sequence:* (DEST) = Address of start of buffer

   (A) = Value

   JSR   BXASB

   (Return w/characters stored in buffer)

IV. *Volatility:* All registers used.

V. *Notes:* On return (DEST) points to last ASCII character stored plus one. Continuing calls may be made to BXASB with the returned pointer in DEST to convert additional values. Location DEST assumed to be in page 0 and specifying a 16-bit address (LS byte followed by MS byte).

Loc	Contents	Label	Operand	Arguments	Comments
200	A0 00	BXASB	LDY	#0	INITIALIZE INDEX
202	A2 30	LOOP	LDX	#$30	ASCII ZERO
204	0A		ASL	A	SHIFT OUT BIT
205	90 01		BCC	NOC	GO IF C=0
207	E8		INX		ASCII ONE
208	48	NOC	PHA		SAVE PARTIAL VALUE
209	8A		TXA		
20A	91 XX		STA	(DEST),Y	STORE ASCII CHARACTER
20C	68		PLA		RESTORE PARTIAL VALUE
20D	C8		INY		
20E	C0 08		CPY	#8	TEST FOR DONE
210	D0 F0		BNE	LOOP	GO IF NOT DONE
212	A5 XX		LDA	DEST	GET LS ADDRESS
214	18		CLC		CLEAR CARRY FOR ADD
215	69 08		ADC	#8	BUMP TO NEXT CHAR POS
217	85 XX		STA	DEST	
219	90 02		BCC	NOC1	GO IF NO CARRY
21B	E6 YY		INC	DEST+1	CARRY TO MS ADDRESS
21D	60	NOC1	RTS		RETURN

BXASD 8080

I. *Name:* BXASD   Binary to ASCII Decimal Subroutine for 8080
II. *Description:* This subroutine converts a 16-bit double-precision binary value to five ASCII decimal digits and stores the result in a specified five-byte memory buffer. Reentrant.
III. *Calling Sequence:* (D,E) = Address of start of buffer
   (H,L) = Value
   CALL BXASD
   (Return with characters stored in buffer)
IV. *Volatility:* All registers used. (H,L) points to last ASCII character stored plus one on return.
V. *Notes:* The most significant bit in each ASCII character is set to zero. User requirements may be different.
   Continuing calls may be made to BXASD with the returned pointer in H,L to convert additional decimal values.

Loc	Contents	Label	Operand	Arguments	Comments
000	023	BXASD	INX	D	
001	023		INX	D	
002	023		INX	D	
003	023		INX	D	POINT TO LS CHAR
004	325		PUSH	D	SAVE LAST POSITION
005	016 005		MVI	C,5	SETUP COUNT
007	006 012		MVI	B,10	DIVISOR
011	315 XXX XXX*	LOOP	CALL	UNSPD	DIVIDE BY 10
014	306 060		ADI	060	CONVERT TO ASCII
016	022		STAX	D	STORE IN BUFFER
017	033		DCX	D	POINT TO HIGHER ORDER
020	015		DCR	C	DECREMENT COUNT
021	302 011 000		JNZ	LOOP	GO IF NOT DONE
024	321		POP	D	
025	023		INX	D	POINT TO LAST+1
026	311		RET		

BXASD 6800

I. *Name:* BXASD   Binary to ASCII Decimal Subroutine for 6800
II. *Description:* This subroutine converts a 16-bit double-precision binary value to five ASCII decimal digits and stores the result in a specified five-byte memory buffer.
III. *Calling Sequence:* (X) = Address of start of buffer
                       (A,B) = Value
                       JSR   BXASD
                       (Return with characters stored in buffer)
IV. *Volatility:* All registers used.
V. *Notes:* The most significant bit in each ASCII character is set to zero. User requirements may be different.
        Continuing calls may be made to BXASD with the returned pointer in X to convert additional decimal values.

Loc	Contents	Label	Operand	Arguments	Comments
100	DF XX	BXASD	STX	TEMP1	SAVE FOR COMPARE
102	08		INX		
103	08		INX		
104	08		INX		
105	08		INX		POINT TO LAST CHAR POS
106	97 YY		STAA	DVDN	STORE VALUE FOR DVD
108	D7 ZZ		STAB	DVDN+1	
10A	86 0A		LDAA	#10	SETUP DIVISOR
10C	97 WW		STAA	DVSR	
10E	DF VV	LOOP	STX	TEMPC	SAVE FOR DVD
110	BD XX XX*		JSR	UNSPD	DIVIDE BY 10
113	DE VV		LDX	TEMPC	RESTORE X
115	96 UU		LDAA	RMNDR	GET REMAINDER
117	8B 30		ADAA	#$30	CONVERT TO ASCII
119	A7 00		STAA	X	STORE
11B	09		DEX		POINT TO NXT HIGHER
11C	9C XX		CPX	TEMP1	TEST FOR DONE
11E	2C EE		BGE	LOOP	GO IF NOT DONE
120	DE XX		LDX	TEMP1	RETRIEVE INDEX
122	08		INX		
123	08		INX		
124	08		INX		
125	08		INX		
126	08		INX		POINT TO LAST PLUS 1
127	39		RTS		RETURN

BXASD 6502

I. *Name:* BXASD   Binary to ASCII Decimal Subroutine for 6502
II. *Description:* See BXASD 6800.
III. *Calling Sequence:* (DEST) = Address of start of buffer
    (DPVAL,DPVAL+1) = Value
    JSR   BXASD
    (Return with characters stored in buffer)
IV. *Volatility:* X register not used.
V. *Notes:* See BXASD 6800. Pointer in DEST. DEST assumed to
    be in page 0 and specifying a 16-bit address (LS byte fol-
    lowed by MS byte).

Loc	Contents	Label	Operand	Arguments	Comments
200	A0 05	BXASD	LDY	#4	INDEX TO LAST POSTN
202	A5 XX		LDA	DPVAL	
204	85 VV		STA	DVDN	MS BYTE TO DIVDND
206	A5 YY		LDA	DPVAL+1	
208	85 WW		STA	DVDN+1	LS BYTE TO DVDND
20A	A9 0A		LDA	#10	
20C	85 UU		STA	DVSR	10 TO DIVISOR
20E	20 XX XX*	LOOP	JSR	UNSPD	DIVIDE BY 10
211	A5 TT		LDA	RMNDR	GET REMAINDER
213	18		CLC		CLEAR C FOR ADD
214	69 30		ADC	#$30	CONVERT TO ASCII
216	91 RR		STA	(DEST),Y	STORE ASCII CHAR
218	88		DEY		POINT TO NEXT
219	10 F3		BPL	LOOP	GO IF NOT DONE
21B	A5 RR		LDA	DEST	DONE
21D	18		CLC		CLEAR C FOR ADD
21E	69 06		ADC	#6	POINT TO LAST + 1
220	90 02		BCC	NOC	GO IF NO CARRY
222	E6 SS		INC	DEST+1	BUMP MS ADDRESS
224	60	NOC	RTS		RETURN

BXASO 8080

I. *Name:* BXASO   Binary to ASCII Octal Subroutine for 8080

II. *Description:* This subroutine converts a 16-bit double-precision binary value to six ASCII octal digits and stores the ASCII characters in a specified six-byte memory buffer. Reentrant.

III. *Calling Sequence:* (H,L) = Address of start of buffer
                        (B,C) = Value
                        CALL   BXASO
                        (Return with characters stored in buffer)

IV. *Volatility:* All registers returned with original values except H,L.
          (H,L) points to last ASCII character stored plus one.

V. *Notes:* The most significant bit in each ASCII character is set to a zero. User requirements may be different.

      Continuing calls may be made to BXASO with the pointer in H,L to convert additional octal values.

Loc	Contents	Label	Operand	Arguments	Comments
000	365	BXASO	PUSH	PSW	SAVE A
001	305		PUSH	B	SAVE B,C
002	325		PUSH	D	SAVE D,E
003	026 007		MVI	D,7	INITIALIZE INDEX
005	175		MOV	A,L	
006	306 006		ADI	6	BUMP POINTER
010	322 014 000		JNC	NOC	GO IF NO CARRY
013	044		INR	H	
014	157	NOC	MOV	L,A	
015	345		PUSH	H	SAVE LAST + 1
016	025	LOOP	DCR	D	DECREMENT INDEX
017	312 045 000		JZ	DONE	GO IF DONE
022	053		DCX	H	POINT TO NEXT CHAR
023	076 007		MVI	A,7	LOAD MASK
025	241		ANA	C	GET NEXT DIGIT
026	306 060		ADI	060	CONVERT TO ASCII
030	167		MOV	M,A	STORE
031	315 052 000		CALL	SHIFT	
034	315 052 000		CALL	SHIFT	
037	315 052 000		CALL	SHIFT	
042	303 016 000		JMP	LOOP	CONTINUE
045	341	DONE	POP	H	POINT TO NEXT
046	321		POP	D	RESTORE D,E
047	301		POP	B	RESTORE B,C
050	361		POP	PSW	RESTORE A
051	311		RET		
052	247	SHIFT	ANA	A	ZERO CARRY
053	170		MOV	A,B	FOR SHIFT
054	037		RAR		SHIFT B,C RIGHT
055	107		MOV	B,A	
056	171		MOV	A,C	
057	037		RAR		
060	117		MOV	C,A	
061	311		RET		

BXASH 8080

I. *Name:* BXASH   Binary to ASCII Hexadecimal Subroutine for 8080
II. *Description:* This subroutine converts an 8-bit binary value to two ASCII hexadecimal digits and stores the ASCII characters in a specified two-byte memory buffer.
III. *Calling Sequence:* (H,L) = Address of start of buffer
                      (B) = Value
                      CALL BXASH
                      (Return with characters stored in buffer)
IV. *Volatility:* All registers returned with original values except H,L. (H,L) points to last ASCII character stored plus one.
V. *Notes:* Continuing calls may be made to BXASH with the returned pointer in H,L to convert additional binary values to hexadecimal.

Loc	Contents	Label	Operand	Arguments	Comments
000	365	BXASH	PUSH	PSW	SAVE A
001	305		PUSH	B	SAVE B,C
002	076 017		MVI	A,017	MASK
004	240		ANA	B	GET 2ND DIGIT
005	365		PUSH	PSW	
006	170		MOV	A,B	
007	017		RRC		
010	017		RRC		
011	017		RRC		
012	017		RRC		SHIFT RIGHT 4
013	346 017		ANI	017	GET FIRST DIGIT
015	315 033 000		CALL	CVERT	CONVERT
020	167		MOV	M,A	STORE
021	043		INX	H	POINT TO NEXT
022	361		POP	PSW	RETRIEVE 2ND DIGIT
023	315 033 000		CALL	CVERT	CONVERT
026	167		MOV	M,A	STORE
027	043		INX	H	FOR RETURN
030	301		POP	B	RESTORE B,C
031	361		POP	PSW	RESTORE A
032	311		RET		
033	376 012	CVERT	CPI	10	TEST FOR A—F
035	372 042 000		JM	NAD	GO IF NO ADJUST
040	306 007		ADI	7	
042	306 060	NAD	ADI	060	CONVERT TO ASCII
044	311		RET		

BXASH 6800

I. *Name:* BXASH   Binary to ASCII Hexadecimal Subroutine for 6800

II. *Description:* See BXASH 8080. Reentrant.

III. *Calling Sequence:* (X) = Address of start of buffer
    (A) = Value
    JSR   BXASH
    (Return with characters stored in buffer)

IV. *Volatility:* B accumulator not used. (X) points to the last ASCII character stored plus one.

V. *Notes:* Continuing calls may be made to BXASH with the returned pointer in X to convert additional binary values to hexadecimal.

Loc	Contents	Label	Operand	Arguments	Comments
100	37	BXASH	PSHB		SAVE B
101	16		TAB		
102	8D 11		BSR	CVERT	CONVERT TO ASCII
104	36		PSHA		SAVE CHARACTER
105	17		TBA		
106	44		LSRA		
107	44		LSRA		
108	44		LSRA		
109	44		LSRA		ALIGN FOR CONVERT
10A	8D 09		BSR	CVERT	CONVERT TO ASCII
10C	A7 00		STAA	X	FIRST CHARACTER
10E	32		PULA		
10F	08		INX		BUMP TO NEXT BYTE
110	A7 00		STAA	X	SECOND CHARACTER
112	08		INX		BUMP FOR RETURN
113	33		PULB		RESTORE B
114	39		RTS		RETURN
115	84 0F	CVERT	ANDA	#$F	GET 0 — 15
117	81 0A		CMPA	#10	TEST FOR 0 — 9
119	2B 02		BMI	NAD	GO IF 0 — 9
11B	8B 07		ADDA	#7	ADJUST FOR A — F
11D	8B 30	NAD	ADDA	#$30	CONVERT TO ASCII
11F	39		RTS		RETURN TO BXASH

BXASH 6502

I. *Name:* BXASH   Binary to ASCII Hexadecimal Subroutine for 6502
II. *Description:* See BXASH 8080.
III. *Calling Sequence:* (DEST) = Address of start of buffer
    (A) = Value
    JSR   BXASH
    (Return with characters stored in buffer)
IV. *Volatility:* X register not used.
V. *Notes:* (DEST) points to last character stored plus one on return. Continuing calls may be made to BXASH with the returned pointer in DEST to convert additional binary values to hexadecimal ASCII. DEST is assumed in page 0 specifying a 16-bit address (LS byte followed by MS byte).

Loc	Contents	Label	Operand	Arguments	Comments
200	48	BXASH	PHA		SAVE TWO DIGITS
201	4A		LSR	A	GET MS DIGIT
202	4A		LSR	A	
203	4A		LSR	A	
204	4A		LSR	A	
205	20 21 02		JSR	CVERT	CONVERT TO ASCII
208	A0 00		LDY	#0	
20A	91 XX		STA	(DEST),Y	STORE FIRST CHAR
20C	68		PLA		RESTORE DIGITS
20D	29 0F		AND	#F	GET LS DIGIT
20F	20 21 02		JSR	CVERT	CONVERT TO ASCII
212	C8		INY		
213	91 XX		STA	(DEST),Y	STORE SECOND CHAR
215	A5 XX		LDA	DEST	
217	18		CLC		CLEAR C FOR ADD
218	69 02		ADC	#2	POINT TO NEXT POSTN
21A	85 XX		STA	DEST	
21C	90 02		BCC	NOC	GO IF NO CARRY
21E	E6 YY		INC	DEST+1	BUMP MS ADDRESS
220	60	NOC	RTS		RETURN
221	C9 0A	CVERT	CMP	#10	TEST FOR 0 − 9
223	30 03		BMI	NOAD	GO IF 0 − 9
225	18		CLC		CLEAR C FOR ADD
226	69 07		ADC	#7	
228	69 30	NOAD	ADC	#$30	CONVERT TO ASCII
22A	60		RTS		

MVDAT 8080

  I. *Name:* MVDAT   Move Data Subroutine for the 8080
  II. *Description:* This subroutine moves a block of data from one area of memory to another. Reentrant.
 III. *Calling Sequence:* (B) = Number of bytes to move
                           (D,E) = Address of source block
                           (H,L) = Address of destination block
 IV. *Volatility:* Registers A, B, D, E, and H,L are not restored to their original values. (D,E) points to the last source byte moved plus one. (H,L) points to the last destination address plus one.
  V. *Notes:* The two memory blocks must be nonoverlapping. A number of 0 is considered 256 bytes.

Loc	Contents	Label	Operand	Arguments	Comments
000	032	MVDAT	LDAX	D	GET SOURCE BYTE
001	167		MOV	M,A	MOVE TO DESTINATION
002	005		DCR	B	DECREMENT INDEX
003	310		RZ	B	GO IF DONE
004	043		INX	H	BUMP DESTINATION PNTR
005	023		INX	D	BUMP SOURCE PNTR
006	303 000 000		JMP	MVDAT	CONTINUE

MVDAT 6800

I. *Name:* MVDAT   Move Data Subroutine for 6800
II. *Description:* This subroutine moves a block of data from one area of memory to another. Not reentrant.
III. *Calling Sequence:* (A) = Number of bytes to move
(SRCE) = Address of source block
(DEST) = Address of destination block
JSR   MVDAT
(Return with data moved)
IV. *Volatility:* All registers used.
V. *Notes:* The two memory blocks must be nonoverlapping. Locations SRCE and DEST are assumed in page 0 at locations XX and YY, respectively. A count of 0 is considered 256.

Loc	Contents	Label	Operand	Arguments	Comments
100	DE XX	MVDAT	LDX	SRCE	SOURCE POINTER
102	E6 00		LDAB	X	GET SOURCE BYTE
104	DE YY		LDX	DEST	DESTINATION PNTR
106	E7 00		STAB	X	STORE BYTE
108	4A		DECA		DECREMENT #
109	27 0C		BEQ	DONE	GO IF DONE
10B	DE XX		LDX	SRCE	BUMP SOURCE POINTER
10D	08		INX		
10E	DF XX		STX	SRCE	
110	DE YY		LDX	DEST	BUMP DEST POINTER
112	08		INX		
113	DF YY		STX	DEST	
115	20 E9		BRA	MVDAT	CONTINUE
117	39	DONE	RTS		RETURN

MVDAT 6502

I. *Name:* MVDAT   Move Data Subroutine for 6502

II. *Description:* This subroutine moves a block of data from one area of memory to another. Not reentrant.

III. *Calling Sequence:* (SRCE) = Address of source block

                               (DEST) = Address of destination block

                               (Y)   = Number of bytes to move

                               JSR   MVDAT

                               (Return with data moved)

IV. *Volatility:* X register not used.

V. *Notes:* The two memory areas must be nonoverlapping. Locations SRCE and DEST are assumed in page 0 at locations XX and YY, respectively, and specify 16-bit addresses (LS byte followed by MS byte). A count of 0 is considered 256.

Loc	Contents	Label	Operand	Arguments	Comments
200	88	MVDAT	DEY		DECREMENT INDEX
201	B1 XX		LDA	(SRCE),Y	GET SOURCE BYTE
203	91 YY		STA	(DEST),Y	STORE
205	C0 00		CPY	#0	TEST FOR DONE
207	D0 F7		BNE	MVDAT	GO IF NOT DONE
209	60		RTS		RETURN

FILLD 8080

I. *Name:* FILLD   Fill Data Subroutine for 8080
II. *Description:* Fills a specified block of memory with a given data
      byte. Reentrant.
III. *Calling Sequence:* (A) = Data to be filled
                         (H,L) = Address of fill area
                         (B) = Number of bytes to fill
                         JSR   FILLD
                         (Return with area filled)
IV. *Volatility:* All registers except H,L returned with original con-
      tents.
V. *Notes:* Fills up to 256 bytes. A count of 0 is considered 256.

Loc	Contents	Label	Operand	Arguments	Comments
000	305	FILLD	PUSH	B	SAVE B,C
001	167	LOOP	MOV	M,A	MOVE DATA
002	005		DCR	B	DECREMENT COUNT
003	312 012 000		JZ	DONE	GO IF DONE
006	043		INX	H	INCREMENT POINTER
007	303 001 000		JMP	LOOP	
012	301	DONE	POP	B	RESTORE B,C
013	311		RET		RETURN

FILLD 6800

I. *Name:* FILLD   Fill Data Subroutine for 6800

II. *Description:* Fills a specified block of memory with a given data byte.

III. *Calling Sequence:* (A) = Data to be filled
   (B) = Number of bytes to fill
   (X) = Address of fill area
   JSR   FILLD
   (Return with area filled)

IV. *Volatility:* A register is returned with its original contents.

V. *Notes:* Fills up to 256 bytes. A count of 0 is considered 256.

Loc	Contents	Label	Operand	Arguments	Comments
100	A7 00	FILLD	STAA	X	FILL
102	5A		DECB		DECREMENT COUNT
103	27 03		BEQ	DONE	GO IF DONE
105	08		INX		POINT TO NEXT
106	20 F8		BRA	FILLD	CONTINUE
108	39	DONE	RTS		RETURN

FILLD 6502

I. *Name:* FILLD   Fill Data Subroutine for 6502
II. *Description:* Fills a specified block of memory with a given data byte.
III. *Calling Sequence:* (A) = Data to be filled
          (DEST) = Fill area
          (Y) = Number of bytes to fill
IV. *Volatility:* The X register is returned with its original contents.
V. *Notes:* DEST is assumed in page 0 and is a 16-bit address (LS byte followed by MS byte). A count of 0 is considered 256.

Loc	Contents	Label	Operand	Arguments	Comments
200	88	FILLD	DEY		ADJUST Y
201	91 XX		STA	(DEST),Y	FILL DOWN
203	D0 FB		BNE	FILLD	CONTINUE
205	60		RTS		RETURN

COMST 8080

I. *Name:* COMST   Compare String Subroutine for 8080
II. *Description:* This subroutine enables the comparison of two strings of data in memory. Reentrant.
III. *Calling Sequence:* (B) = Number of bytes in strings
   (D,E) = Address of first byte of string A
   (H,L) = Address of first byte of string B
   CALL   COMST
   (Return with A<0 if string A<string B, A=0 if string A=string B, and A>0 if string A>string B)
IV. *Volatility:* All registers restored to original contents except for A.
V. *Notes:* String may be ASCII or other data. The compare is done with the assumption that the higher-order bytes are of greater weight. Number of bytes may be 1 to 127. Most significant bit of each byte must be 0.

Loc	Contents	Label	Operand	Arguments	Comments
000	305	COMST	PUSH	B	SAVE B,C
001	325		PUSH	D	SAVE D,E
002	345		PUSH	H	SAVE H,L
003	005	CONT	DCR	B	DECREMENT COUNT
004	372 016 000		JM	DONE	GO IF DONE
007	032		LDAX	D	GET BYTE OF STR A
010	226		SUB	M	A:B
011	023		INX	D	BUMP STRING A ADDR
012	043		INX	H	BUMP STRING B ADDR
013	312 003 000		JZ	CONT	GO IF EQUAL
016	341	DONE	POP	H	RESTORE H,L
017	321		POP	D	RESTORE D,E
020	301		POP	B	RESTORE B,C
021	311		RET		RETURN

COMST 6800

I. *Name:* COMST   Compare String Subroutine for 6800

II. *Description:* This subroutine enables the comparison of two strings of data in memory.

III. *Calling Sequence:* (A) = Number of bytes in string
(SRCE) = Address of first byte of string A
(DEST) = Address of first byte of string B
JSR   COMST
(Return with B<0 if string A<string B, B=0 if string A=string B, and B>0 if string A>string B)

IV. *Volatility:* All registers used.

V. *Notes:* String may be ASCII or other data. The compare is done with the assumption that higher-order bytes are of greater weight. Count may be 1 to 127. On return SRCE and DEST point to end of strings + 1. Most significant bit of each byte must be 0.

Loc	Contents	Label	Operand	Arguments	Comments
100	4A	COMST	DECA		DECREMENT COUNT
101	2B 0A		BMI	DONE	GO IF DONE
103	DE XX		LDX	SRCE	GET STRING A PNTR
105	E6 00		LDAB	X	GET NEXT BYTE
107	DE YY		LDX	DEST	GET STRING B PNTR
109	E0 00		SUBB	X	A — B
10B	27 01		BEQ	LOOP	GO IF EQUAL
10D	39	DONE	RTS		RETURN
10E	DE XX	LOOP	LDX	SRCE	BUMP SOURCE POINTER
110	08		INX		
111	DF XX		STX	SRCE	
113	DE YY		LDX	DEST	BUMP DEST POINTER
115	08		INX		
116	DF YY		STX	DEST	
118	20 E6		BRA	COMST	

COMST 6502

I. *Name:* COMST   Compare String Subroutine for 6502

II. *Description:* This subroutine enables the comparison of two strings of data in memory.

III. *Calling Sequence:* (X) = Number of bytes in string
     (SRCE) = Address of first byte of string A
     (DEST) = Address of first byte of string B
     JSR   COMST
     (Return with A<0 if string A<B, A=0 if string A=string B, A>0 if string A> string B)

IV. *Volatility:* All registers used.

V. *Notes:* String may be ASCII or other data. The compare is done with the assumption that higher-order bytes are of greater weight. Count may be 1 to 127. SRCE and DEST assumed to page 0 and specifying 16-bit addresses (LS byte followed by MS bytes). Most significant bit of each byte must be 0.

Loc	Contents	Label	Operand	Arguments	Comments
200	A0 FF	COMST	LDY	#FF	
202	C8	LOOP	INY		BUMP INDEX
203	CA		DEX		DECREMENT COUNT
204	30 07		BMI	DONE	
206	38		SEC		SET CARRY FOR SUBT
207	B1 XX		LDA	(SRCE),Y	GET SOURCE BYTE
209	F1 YY		SBC	(DEST),Y	SOURCE—DEST
20B	F0 F5		BEQ	LOOP	GO IF NOT DONE
20D	60	DONE	RTS		GO IF DONE

SRTAB 8080

I. *Name:* SRTAB   Search Table Subroutine for 8080

II. *Description:* This subroutine searches a table of N entries with M bytes per entry for a caller-specified 8-bit key.

III. *Calling Sequence:* (A) = 8-bit key value
                         (H,L) = Address of table start
                         (B) = Number of bytes per entry
                         (C) = Number of entries in table
                         CALL   SRTAB
                         [Return with H,L pointing to entry if found, otherwise (H,L)=−1].

IV. *Volatility:* All registers returned with original values except for H,L and C. C is the current entry count.

V. *Notes:* If the table contains more than one entry that matches the key, another call may immediately be made to SRTAB after recording the position of the previous entry without reinitializing parameters.
Table may be 1 to 127 entries.

Loc	Contents	Label	Operand	Arguments	Comments
000	015	SRTAB	DCR	C	DECREMENT ENTRY CNT
001	372 017 000		JM	NFND	GO IF DONE — NOT FND
004	276		CMP	M	COMPARE ENTRY
005	310		RZ		GO IF FOUND
006	305		PUSH	B	SAVE B,C
007	110		MOV	C,B	NUMBER OF BYTES
010	006 000		MVI	B,O	
012	011		DAD	B	BUMP POINTER
013	301		POP	B	RESTORE B,C
014	303 000 000		JMP	SRTAB	CONTINUE
017	041 377 377	NFND	LXI	H,−1	MARK NOT FOUND
022	311		RET		

SRTAB 6800

I. *Name:* SRTAB   Search Table Subroutine for 6800

II. *Description:* This subroutine searches a table of *N* entries with *M* bytes per entry for a caller-specified 8-bit key.

III. *Calling Sequence:*   (A) = 8-bit key value
    (DEST) = Address of table start
    (NBYTS) = Number of bytes per entry
    (NENT) = Number of entries in table
    JSR   SRTAB
    [Return with (DEST)=address of entry if found or −1]

IV. *Volatility:* Does not use B register.

V. *Notes:* If the table contains more than one entry that matches the key, another call may immediately be made to SRTAB after recording the position of the previous entry without reinitializing parameters.

Table may be 1 to 127 entries.

Loc	Contents	Label	Operand	Arguments	Comments
100	37	SRTAB	PSHB		SAVE B
101	7A 00 ZZ	LOOP	DEC	NENT	DECREMENT ENTRY CNT
104	2B 13		BMI	NFND	NOT FOUND
106	DE XX		LDX	DEST	SETUP INDEX
108	A1 00		CMPA	X	TEST
10A	27 13		BEQ	FND	GO IF FND
10C	D6 YY		LDAB	DEST+1	LS ADDRESS
10E	DB WW		ADDB	NBYTS	BUMP
110	D7 YY		STAB	DEST+1	NEW ADDRESS
112	24 ED		BCC	LOOP	GO IF NO CARRY
114	7C 00 XX		INC	DEST	CARRY TO HIGHER ORDER
117	20 E8		BRA	LOOP	CONTINUE
119	C6 FF	NFND	LDAB	#−1	NOT FND FLAG
11B	D7 XX		STAB	DEST	
11D	D7 YY		STAB	DEST+1	
11F	33	FND	PULB		RESTORE B
120	39		RTS		

SRTAB 6502

I. *Name:* SRTAB   Search Table Subroutine for 6502

II. *Description:* This subroutine searches a table of *N* entries with *M* bytes per entry for a caller-specified 8-bit key.

III. *Calling Sequence:* (A) = 8-bit key value
       (DEST) = Address of table start
       (NBYTS) = Number of bytes per entry
       (X) = Number of entries in table
       JSR   SRTAB
       [Return with (DEST)=address of entry if found, otherwise = −1]

IV. *Volatility:* All registers used.

V. *Notes:* If the table contains more than one entry that matches the key, another call may immediately be made to SRTAB after recording the position of the previous entry without reinitializing parameters. Location DEST assumed in page 0 specifying a 16-bit address (LS byte followed by MS byte).

Loc	Contents	Label	Operand	Arguments	Comments
200	A0 00	SRTAB	LDY	#0	INITIALIZE INDEX
202	CA	LOOP	DEX		DECREMENT NUMBER OF ENTRIES
203	30 0E		BMI	NFND	GO IF AT END
205	D1 XX		CMP	(DEST),Y	COMPARE TO NEXT
207	F0 11		BEQ	FND	GO IF FOUND
209	48		PHA		SAVE KEY
20A	98		TYA		
20B	18		CLC		CLEAR CARRY FOR ADD
20C	65 ZZ		ADC	NBYTS	ADD CURRENT # BYTES
20E	A8		TAY		NEXT INDEX
20F	68		PLA		RESTORE KEY
210	4C 02 02		JMP	LOOP	CONTINUE
213	A9 FF	NFND	LDA	#−1	FLAG FOR NOT FND
215	85 XX		STA	DEST	
217	85 YY		STA	DEST+1	
219	60		RTS		
21A	48	FND	PHA		SAVE KEY
21B	98		TYA		GET INDEX
21C	18		CLC		CLEAR CARRY FOR ADD
21D	65 XX		ADC	DEST	ADD LS ADDRESS
21F	85 XX		STA	DEST	
221	90 02		BCC	NOC	GO IF NO CARRY
223	E6 YY		INC	DEST+1	CARRY TO MS BYTE
225	68	NOC	PLA		RESTORE KEY
226	60		RTS		RETURN

RANDM 8080

I. *Name:* RANDM   Random Number Generator for 8080

II. *Description:* Finds a pseudo-random number by multiplying the last pseudo-random number by 5. Only the least significant 16 bits are saved, in effect performing a modulus 64K operation.

$$R_{n+1} = K\,R_n \bmod 2^{16}$$

III. *Calling Sequence:* (H,L) = seed (first R_n) or last random number

CALL   RANDM

[Return with (H,L) = next pseudo-random number]

IV. *Volatility:* All registers returned with original contents except for H,L.

V. *Notes:* Starting with an odd seed will generate at least 16K pseudo-random numbers without a repeat of the series.

Loc	Contents	Label	Operand	Arguments	Comments
000	325	RANDM	PUSH	D	SAVE D,E
001	345		PUSH	H	TIMES 1
002	051		DAD	H	TIMES 2
003	051		DAD	H	TIMES 4
004	321		POP	D	
005	031		DAD	D	TIMES 5
006	321		POP	D	RESTORE D,E
007	311		RET		RETURN

RANDM 6800

I. *Name:* RANDM   Random Number Generator for 6800
II. *Description:* See RANDM 8080. Not reentrant.
III. *Calling Sequence:* (A,B) = Double-precision seed or last random number
               JSR   RANDM
               [Return with (A,B) = next pseudo-random number]
IV. *Volatility:* All registers used.
V. *Notes:* See RANDM 8080.
               Asterisk marks address of SHIFT subroutine.

Loc	Contents	Label	Operand	Arguments	Comments
100	36	RANDM	PSHA		SAVE A FOR X 5
101	37		PSHB		SAVE B FOR X 5
102	CE FF FE		LDX	#—2	SETUP FOR SHIFT
105	BD XX XX*		JSR	SHIFT	TIMES 4
108	C4 FC		ANDB	#$FC	MAKE LOGICAL SHIFT
10A	B7 01 15		STAA	TEMP1	COULD BE PAGE 0
10D	32		PULA		GET LS BYTE
10E	1B		ABA		FIND LS PRODUCT
10F	16		TAB		TRANSFER TO LS REG
110	32		PULA		GET MS BYTE
111	B9 01 15		ADCA	TEMP1	FIND MS PRODUCT
114	39		RTS		RETURN
115		TEMP1	RMB	1	TEMPORARY

RANDM 6502

I. *Name:* RANDM   Random Number Generator for 6502
II. *Description:* See RANDM 8080. Not reentrant.
III. *Calling Sequence:* (MSDP,LSDP) = Double-precision seed or
last random number

JSR   RANDM

[Return with (MSDP,LSDP) = next pseudo-
random number]

IV. *Volatility:* All registers used.
V. *Notes:* See RANDM 8080.

Asterisk marks address of SHIFT subroutine.

Loc	Contents	Label	Operand	Arguments	Comments
200	A5 XX	RANDM	LDA	MSDP	SAVE FOR X 1
202	48		PHA		
203	A5 YY		LDA	LSDP	
205	48		PHA		
206	A2 FE		LDX	#—2	SETUP FOR SHIFT
208	20 ZZ ZZ*		JSR	SHIFT	SHIFT LEFT TWO
20B	A5 YY		LDA	LSDP	
20D	29 FC		AND	#$FC	MAKE LOGICAL
20F	85 YY		STA	LSDP	
211	68		PLA		PULL LSDP
212	18		CLC		CLEAR CARRY
213	65 YY		ADC	LSDP	TIMES FIVE LS BYTE
215	85 YY		STA	LSDP	
217	68		PLA		PULL MSDP
218	65 XX		ADC	MSDP	TIMES FIVE MS BYTE
21A	85 XX		STA	MSDP	
21C	60		RTS		

Intel 8080 Instruction Set

Mnemonic	Description	D7	D6	D5	D4	D3	D2	D1	D0	Clock Cycles [2]
MOV r1,r2	Move register to register	0	1	D	D	D	S	S	S	5
MOV M,r	Move register to memory	0	1	1	1	0	S	S	S	7
MOV r,M	Move memory to register	0	1	D	D	D	1	1	0	7
HLT	Halt	0	1	1	1	0	1	1	0	7
MVI r	Move immediate register	0	0	D	D	D	1	1	0	7
MVI M	Move immediate memory	0	0	1	1	0	1	1	0	10
INR r	Increment register	0	0	D	D	D	1	0	0	5
DCR r	Decrement register	0	0	D	D	D	1	0	1	5
INR M	Increment memory	0	0	1	1	0	1	0	0	10
DCR M	Decrement memory	0	0	1	1	0	1	0	1	10
ADD r	Add register to A	1	0	0	0	0	S	S	S	4
ADC r	Add register to A with carry	1	0	0	0	1	S	S	S	4
SUB r	Subtract register from A	1	0	0	1	0	S	S	S	4
SBB r	Subtract register from A with borrow	1	0	0	1	1	S	S	S	4
ANA r	And register with A	1	0	1	0	0	S	S	S	4
XRA r	Exclusive Or register with A	1	0	1	0	1	S	S	S	4
ORA r	Or register with A	1	0	1	1	0	S	S	S	4
CMP r	Compare register with A	1	0	1	1	1	S	S	S	4
ADD M	Add memory to A	1	0	0	0	0	1	1	0	7
ADC M	Add memory to A with carry	1	0	0	0	1	1	1	0	7
SUB M	Subtract memory from A	1	0	0	1	0	1	1	0	7
SBB M	Subtract memory from A with borrow	1	0	0	1	1	1	1	0	7
ANA M	And memory with A	1	0	1	0	0	1	1	0	7
XRA M	Exclusive Or memory with A	1	0	1	0	1	1	1	0	7
ORA M	Or memory with A	1	0	1	1	0	1	1	0	7
CMP M	Compare memory with A	1	0	1	1	1	1	1	0	7
ADI	Add immediate to A	1	1	0	0	0	1	1	0	7
ACI	Add immediate to A with carry	1	1	0	0	1	1	1	0	7

Mnemonic	Description	D7	D6	D5	D4	D3	D2	D1	D0	Clock Cycles [2]
RZ	Return on zero	1	1	0	0	1	0	0	0	5/11
RNZ	Return on no zero	1	1	0	0	0	0	0	0	5/11
RP	Return on positive	1	1	1	1	0	0	0	0	5/11
RM	Return on minus	1	1	1	1	1	0	0	0	5/11
RPE	Return on parity even	1	1	1	0	1	0	0	0	5/11
RPO	Return on parity odd	1	1	1	0	0	0	0	0	5/11
RST	Restart	1	1	A	A	A	1	1	1	11
IN	Input	1	1	0	1	1	0	1	1	10
OUT	Output	1	1	0	1	0	0	1	1	10
LXI B	Load immediate register Pair B & C	0	0	0	0	0	0	0	1	10
LXI D	Load immediate register Pair D & E	0	0	0	1	0	0	0	1	10
LXI H	Load immediate register Pair H & L	0	0	1	0	0	0	0	1	10
LXI SP	Load immediate stack pointer	0	0	1	1	0	0	0	1	10
PUSH B	Push register Pair B & C on stack	1	1	0	0	0	1	0	1	11
PUSH D	Push register Pair D & E on stack	1	1	0	1	0	1	0	1	11
PUSH H	Push register Pair H & L on stack	1	1	1	0	0	1	0	1	11
PUSH PSW	Push A and Flags on stack	1	1	1	1	0	1	0	1	11
POP B	Pop register pair B & C off stack	1	1	0	0	0	0	0	1	10
POP D	Pop register pair D & E off stack	1	1	0	1	0	0	0	1	10
POP H	Pop register pair H & L off stack	1	1	1	0	0	0	0	1	10

Mnemonic	Description	Clock Cycles
SUI	Subtract immediate from A	7
SBI	Subtract immediate from A with borrow	7
ANI	And immediate with A	7
XRI	Exclusive Or immediate with A	7
ORI	Or immediate with A	7
CPI	Compare immediate with A	7
RLC	Rotate A left	4
RRC	Rotate A right	4
RAL	Rotate A left through carry	4
RAR	Rotate A right through carry	4
JMP	Jump unconditional	10
JC	Jump on carry	10
JNC	Jump on no carry	10
JZ	Jump on zero	10
JNZ	Jump on no zero	10
JP	Jump on positive	10
JM	Jump on minus	10
JPE	Jump on parity even	10
JPO	Jump on parity odd	10
CALL	Call unconditional	17
CC	Call on carry	11/17
CNC	Call on no carry	11/17
CZ	Call on zero	11/17
CNZ	Call on no zero	11/17
CP	Call on positive	11/17
CM	Call on minus	11/17
CPE	Call on parity even	11/17
CPO	Call on parity odd	11/17
RET	Return	10
RC	Return on carry	5/11
RNC	Return on no carry	5/11

Mnemonic	Description	Clock Cycles
POP PSW	Pop A and Flags off stack	10
STA	Store A direct	13
LDA	Load A direct	13
XCHG	Exchange D & E, H & L Registers	4
XTHL	Exchange top of stack, H & L	18
SPHL	H & L to stack pointer	5
PCHL	H & L to program counter	5
DAD B	Add B & C to H & L	10
DAD D	Add D & E to H & L	10
DAD H	Add H & L to H & L	10
DAD SP	Add stack pointer to H & L	10
STAX B	Store A indirect	7
STAX D	Store A indirect	7
LDAX B	Load A indirect	7
LDAX D	Load A indirect	7
INX B	Increment B & C registers	5
INX D	Increment D & E registers	5
INX H	Increment H & L registers	5
INX SP	Increment stack pointer	5
DCX B	Decrement B & C	5
DCX D	Decrement D & E	5
DCX H	Decrement H & L	5
DCX SP	Decrement stack pointer	5
CMA	Complement A	4
STC	Set carry	4
CMC	Complement carry	4
DAA	Decimal adjust A	4
SHLD	Store H & L direct	16
LHLD	Load H & L direct	16
EI	Enable Interrupts	4
DI	Disable interrupt	4
NOP	No-operation	4

NOTES: 1. DDD or SSS – 000 B – 001 C – 010 D – 011 E – 100 H – 101 L – 110 Memory – 111 A.

2. Two possible cycle times, (5/11) indicate instruction cycles dependent on condition flags.

Courtesy Intel Corp.

Motorola MC6800
Instruction Set

TABLE 3 – ACCUMULATOR AND MEMORY INSTRUCTIONS

OPERATIONS	MNEMONIC	IMMED OP	~	=	DIRECT OP	~	=	INDEX OP	~	=	EXTND OP	~	=	IMPLIED OP	~	=	BOOLEAN/ARITHMETIC OPERATION (All register labels refer to contents)	5 H	4 I	3 N	2 Z	1 V	0 C
Add	ADDA	8B	2	2	9B	3	2	AB	5	2	BB	4	3				$A + M \rightarrow A$	↕	•	↕	↕	↕	↕
	ADDB	CB	2	2	DB	3	2	EB	5	2	FB	4	3				$B + M \rightarrow B$	↕	•	↕	↕	↕	↕
Add Acmltrs	ABA													1B	2	1	$A + B \rightarrow A$	↕	•	↕	↕	↕	↕
Add with Carry	ADCA	89	2	2	99	3	2	A9	5	2	B9	4	3				$A + M + C \rightarrow A$	↕	•	↕	↕	↕	↕
	ADCB	C9	2	2	D9	3	2	E9	5	2	F9	4	3				$B + M + C \rightarrow B$	↕	•	↕	↕	↕	↕
And	ANDA	84	2	2	94	3	2	A4	5	2	B4	4	3				$A \cdot M \rightarrow A$	•	•	↕	↕	R	•
	ANDB	C4	2	2	D4	3	2	E4	5	2	F4	4	3				$B \cdot M \rightarrow B$	•	•	↕	↕	R	•
Bit Test	BITA	85	2	2	95	3	2	A5	5	2	B5	4	3				$A \cdot M$	•	•	↕	↕	R	•
	BITB	C5	2	2	D5	3	2	E5	5	2	F5	4	3				$B \cdot M$	•	•	↕	↕	R	•
Clear	CLR							6F	7	2	7F	6	3				$00 \rightarrow M$	•	•	R	S	R	R
	CLRA													4F	2	1	$00 \rightarrow A$	•	•	R	S	R	R
	CLRB													5F	2	1	$00 \rightarrow B$	•	•	R	S	R	R
Compare	CMPA	81	2	2	91	3	2	A1	5	2	B1	4	3				$A - M$	•	•	↕	↕	↕	↕
	CMPB	C1	2	2	D1	3	2	E1	5	2	F1	4	3				$B - M$	•	•	↕	↕	↕	↕
Compare Acmltrs	CBA													11	2	1	$A - B$	•	•	↕	↕	↕	↕
Complement, 1's	COM							63	7	2	73	6	3				$\bar{M} \rightarrow M$	•	•	↕	↕	R	S
	COMA													43	2	1	$\bar{A} \rightarrow A$	•	•	↕	↕	R	S
	COMB													53	2	1	$\bar{B} \rightarrow B$	•	•	↕	↕	R	S
Complement, 2's (Negate)	NEG							60	7	2	70	6	3				$00 - M \rightarrow M$	•	•	↕	↕	①	②
	NEGA													40	2	1	$00 - A \rightarrow A$	•	•	↕	↕	①	②
	NEGB													50	2	1	$00 - B \rightarrow B$	•	•	↕	↕	①	②
Decimal Adjust, A	DAA													19	2	1	Converts Binary Add. of BCD Characters into BCD Format	•	•	↕	↕	①	③
Decrement	DEC							6A	7	2	7A	6	3				$M - 1 \rightarrow M$	•	•	↕	↕	④	•
	DECA													4A	2	1	$A - 1 \rightarrow A$	•	•	↕	↕	④	•
	DECB													5A	2	1	$B - 1 \rightarrow B$	•	•	↕	↕	④	•
Exclusive OR	EORA	88	2	2	98	3	2	A8	5	2	B8	4	3				$A \oplus M \rightarrow A$	•	•	↕	↕	R	•
	EORB	C8	2	2	D8	3	2	E8	5	2	F8	4	3				$B \oplus M \rightarrow B$	•	•	↕	↕	R	•
Increment	INC							6C	7	2	7C	6	3				$M + 1 \rightarrow M$	•	•	↕	↕	⑤	•
	INCA													4C	2	1	$A + 1 \rightarrow A$	•	•	↕	↕	⑤	•
	INCB													5C	2	1	$B + 1 \rightarrow B$	•	•	↕	↕	⑤	•
Load Acmltr	LDAA	86	2	2	96	3	2	A6	5	2	B6	4	3				$M \rightarrow A$	•	•	↕	↕	R	•
	LDAB	C6	2	2	D6	3	2	E6	5	2	F6	4	3				$M \rightarrow B$	•	•	↕	↕	R	•
Or, Inclusive	ORAA	8A	2	2	9A	3	2	AA	5	2	BA	4	3				$A + M \rightarrow A$	•	•	↕	↕	R	•
	ORAB	CA	2	2	DA	3	2	EA	5	2	FA	4	3				$B + M \rightarrow B$	•	•	↕	↕	R	•

242

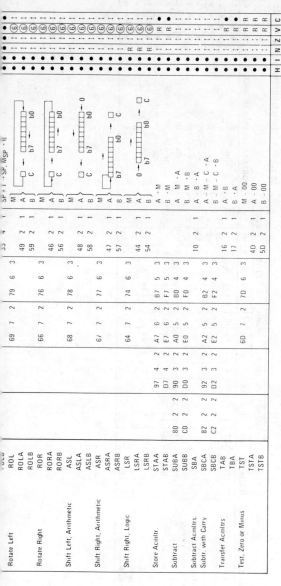

		IMMED			DIRECT			INDEX			EXTEND			IMPLIED			BOOLEAN/ARITHMETIC OPERATION	H	I	N	Z	V	C
		OP	~	=	OP	~	=	OP	~	=	OP	~	=	OP	~	=							
Rotate Left	ROL							69	7	2	79	6	3				M	•	•	↕	↕	⑥	↕
	ROLA													49	2	1	A	•	•	↕	↕	⑥	↕
	ROLB													59	2	1	B	•	•	↕	↕	⑥	↕
Rotate Right	ROR							66	7	2	76	6	3				M	•	•	↕	↕	⑥	↕
	RORA													46	2	1	A	•	•	↕	↕	⑥	↕
	RORB													56	2	1	B	•	•	↕	↕	⑥	↕
Shift Left, Arithmetic	ASL							68	7	2	78	6	3				M	•	•	↕	↕	⑥	↕
	ASLA													48	2	1	A	•	•	↕	↕	⑥	↕
	ASLB													58	2	1	B	•	•	↕	↕	⑥	↕
Shift Right, Arithmetic	ASR							67	7	2	77	6	3				M	•	•	↕	↕	⑥	↕
	ASRA													47	2	1	A	•	•	↕	↕	⑥	↕
	ASRB													57	2	1	B	•	•	↕	↕	⑥	↕
Shift Right, Logic	LSR							64	7	2	74	6	3				M	•	•	R	↕	⑥	↕
	LSRA													44	2	1	A	•	•	R	↕	⑥	↕
	LSRB													54	2	1	B	•	•	R	↕	⑥	↕
Store Acmltr.	STAA				97	4	2	A7	6	2	B7	5	3				A → M	•	•	↕	↕	R	•
	STAB				D7	4	2	E7	6	2	F7	5	3				B → M	•	•	↕	↕	R	•
Subtract	SUBA	80	2	2	90	3	2	A0	5	2	B0	4	3				A - M	•	•	↕	↕	↕	↕
	SUBB	C0	2	2	D0	3	2	E0	5	2	F0	4	3				B - M	•	•	↕	↕	↕	↕
Subtract Acmltrs.	SBA													10	2	1	A - B	•	•	↕	↕	↕	↕
Subtr. with Carry	SBCA	82	2	2	92	3	2	A2	5	2	B2	4	3				A - M - C → A	•	•	↕	↕	↕	↕
	SBCB	C2	2	2	D2	3	2	E2	5	2	F2	4	3				B - M - C → B	•	•	↕	↕	↕	↕
Transfer Acmltrs	TAB													16	2	1	A → B	•	•	↕	↕	R	•
	TBA													17	2	1	B → A	•	•	↕	↕	R	•
Test, Zero or Minus	TST							6D	7	2	7D	6	3				M - 00	•	•	↕	↕	R	R
	TSTA													4D	2	1	A - 00	•	•	↕	↕	R	R
	TSTB													5D	2	1	B - 00	•	•	↕	↕	R	R

LEGEND:

- OP   Operation Code (Hexadecimal);
- ~   Number of MPU Cycles;
- =   Number of Program Bytes;
- +   Arithmetic Plus;
- -   Arithmetic Minus;
- •   Boolean AND;
- MSP Contents of memory location pointed to be Stack Pointer;

- +   Boolean Inclusive OR;
- ⊙   Boolean Exclusive OR;
- M̄   Complement of M;
- →   Transfer Into;
- 0   Bit = Zero;
- 00   Byte = Zero;

Note — Accumulator addressing mode instructions are included in the column for IMPLIED addressing

CONDITION CODE SYMBOLS:

- H   Half-carry from bit 3;
- I   Interrupt mask
- N   Negative (sign bit)
- Z   Zero (byte)
- V   Overflow, 2's complement
- C   Carry from bit 7
- R   Reset Always
- S   Set Always
- ↕   Test and set if true, cleared otherwise
- •   Not Affected

TABLE 4 – INDEX REGISTER AND STACK MANIPULATION INSTRUCTIONS

POINTER OPERATIONS	MNEMONIC	IMMED OP	~	#	DIRECT OP	~	#	INDEX OP	~	#	EXTND OP	~	#	IMPLIED OP	~	#	BOOLEAN/ARITHMETIC OPERATION	H (5)	I (4)	N (3)	Z (2)	V (1)	C (0)
Compare Index Reg	CPX	8C	3	3	9C	4	2	AC	6	2	BC	5	3				$X_H - M, X_L - (M+1)$	•	•	⑦	↕	⑦	•
Decrement Index Reg	DEX													09	4	1	$X - 1 \to X$	•	•	↕	↕	•	•
Decrement Stack Pntr	DES													34	4	1	$SP - 1 \to SP$	•	•	•	•	•	•
Increment Index Reg	INX													08	4	1	$X + 1 \to X$	•	•	↕	↕	•	•
Increment Stack Pntr	INS													31	4	1	$SP + 1 \to SP$	•	•	•	•	•	•
Load Index Reg	LDX	CE	3	3	DE	4	2	EE	6	2	FE	5	3				$M \to X_H, (M+1) \to X_L$	•	•	⑨	↕	R	•
Load Stack Pntr	LDS	8E	3	3	9E	4	2	AE	6	2	BE	5	3				$M \to SP_H, (M+1) \to SP_L$	•	•	⑨	↕	R	•
Store Index Reg	STX				DF	5	2	EF	7	2	FF	6	3				$X_H \to M, X_L \to (M+1)$	•	•	⑨	↕	R	•
Store Stack Pntr	STS				9F	5	2	AF	7	2	BF	6	3				$SP_H \to M, SP_L \to (M+1)$	•	•	⑨	↕	R	•
Indx Reg → Stack Pntr	TXS													35	4	1	$X - 1 \to SP$	•	•	•	•	•	•
Stack Pntr → Indx Reg	TSX													30	4	1	$SP + 1 \to X$	•	•	•	•	•	•

BOOLEAN/ARITHMETIC OPERATION — COND. CODE REG.

TABLE 5 – JUMP AND BRANCH INSTRUCTIONS

OPERATIONS	MNEMONIC	RELATIVE OP	~	#	INDEX OP	~	#	EXTND OP	~	#	IMPLIED OP	~	#	BRANCH TEST	5 H	4 I	3 N	2 Z	1 V	0 C
Branch Always	BRA	20	4	2										None	•	•	•	•	•	•
Branch If Carry Clear	BCC	24	4	2										$C = 0$	•	•	•	•	•	•
Branch If Carry Set	BCS	25	4	2										$C = 1$	•	•	•	•	•	•
Branch If = Zero	BEQ	27	4	2										$Z = 1$	•	•	•	•	•	•
Branch If ≥ Zero	BGE	2C	4	2										$N \oplus V = 0$	•	•	•	•	•	•
Branch If > Zero	BGT	2E	4	2										$Z + (N \oplus V) = 0$	•	•	•	•	•	•
Branch If Higher	BHI	22	4	2										$C + Z = 0$	•	•	•	•	•	•
Branch If ≤ Zero	BLE	2F	4	2										$Z + (N \oplus V) = 1$	•	•	•	•	•	•
Branch If Lower Or Same	BLS	23	4	2										$C + Z = 1$	•	•	•	•	•	•
Branch If < Zero	BLT	2D	4	2										$N \oplus V = 1$	•	•	•	•	•	•
Branch If Minus	BMI	2B	4	2										$N = 1$	•	•	•	•	•	•
Branch If Not Equal Zero	BNE	26	4	2										$Z = 0$	•	•	•	•	•	•
Branch If Overflow Clear	BVC	28	4	2										$V = 0$	•	•	•	•	•	•
Branch If Overflow Set	BVS	29	4	2										$V = 1$	•	•	•	•	•	•
Branch If Plus	BPL	2A	4	2										$N = 0$	•	•	•	•	•	•
Branch To Subroutine	BSR	8D	8	2										} See Special Operations	•	•	•	•	•	•
Jump	JMP				6E	4	2	7E	3	3					•	•	•	•	•	•
Jump To Subroutine	JSR				AD	8	2	BD	9	3					•	•	•	•	•	•
No Operation	NOP										02	2	1	Advances Prog. Cntr. Only	•	•	•	•	•	•
Return From Interrupt	RTI										3B	10	1		•	⑩				
Return From Subroutine	RTS										39	5	1		•	•	•	•	•	•
Software Interrupt	SWI										3F	12	1	} See Special Operations	•	⑪	•	•	•	•
Wait for Interrupt	WAI										3E	9	1		•	•	•	•	•	•

Courtesy Motorola Semiconductor Products, Inc.

TABLE 6 — CONDITION CODE REGISTER MANIPULATION INSTRUCTIONS

OPERATIONS	MNEMONIC	IMPLIED OP	~	#	BOOLEAN OPERATION	5 H	4 I	3 N	2 Z	1 V	0 C
Clear Carry	CLC	0C	?	1	0 → C	•	•	•	•	•	R
Clear Interrupt Mask	CLI	0E	2	1	0 → I	•	R	•	•	•	•
Clear Overflow	CLV	0A	2	1	0 → V	•	•	•	•	R	•
Set Carry	SEC	0D	2	1	1 → C	•	•	•	•	•	S
Set Interrupt Mask	SEI	0F	2	1	1 → I	•	S	•	•	•	•
Set Overflow	SEV	0B	2	1	1 → V	•	•	•	•	S	•
Acmltr A → CCR	TAP	06	2	1	A → CCR			(12)			
CCR → Acmltr A	TPA	07	2	1	CCR → A	•	•	•	•	•	•

CONDITION CODE REGISTER NOTES:

(Bit set if test is true and cleared otherwise)

1 (Bit V) Test: Result = 10000000?
2 (Bit C) Test: Result = 00000000?
3 (Bit C) Test: Decimal value of most significant BCD Character greater than nine? (Not cleared if previously set.)
4 (Bit V) Test: Operand = 10000000 prior to execution?
5 (Bit V) Test: Operand = 01111111 prior to execution?
6 (Bit V) Test: Set equal to result of N⊕C after shift has occurred.
7 (Bit N) Test: Sign bit of most significant (MS) byte = 1?
8 (Bit V) Test: 2's complement overflow from subtraction of MS bytes?
9 (Bit N) Test: Result less than zero? (Bit 15 = 1)
10 (All) Load Condition Code Register from Stack. (See Special Operations)
11 (Bit I) Set when interrupt occurs. If previously set, a Non-Maskable Interrupt is required to exit the wait state.
12 (All) Set according to the contents of Accumulator A.

Courtesy Motorola Semiconductor Products, Inc.

246

APPENDIX

C

MOS Technology MCS6502 Instruction Set

INSTRUCTION SET – OP CODES, Execution Time, Memory Requirements

MNEMONIC	OPERATION	IMM OP	IMM N	IMM #	ABS OP	ABS N	ABS #	ZP OP	ZP N	ZP #	ACC OP	ACC N	ACC #	IMPL OP	IMPL N	IMPL #	(IND,X) OP	(IND,X) N	(IND,X) #	ZP,X OP	ZP,X N	ZP,X #	ABS,X OP	ABS,X N	ABS,X #	ABS,Y OP	ABS,Y N	ABS,Y #	(IND),Y OP	(IND),Y N	(IND),Y #	REL OP	REL N	REL #	IND OP	IND N	IND #	ZP,Y OP	ZP,Y N	ZP,Y #	N	Z	C	I	D	V
ADC	A+M+C → A (4)(1)	69	2	2	6D	4	3	65	3	2							61	6	2	75	4	2	7D	4	3	79	4	3	71	5	2										✓	✓	✓	–	–	✓
AND	A∧M→A (1)	29	2	2	2D	4	3	25	3	2							21	6	2	35	4	2	3D	4	3	39	4	3	31	5	2										✓	✓	–	–	–	–
ASL	C ← ☐				0E	6	3	06	5	2	0A	2	1							16	6	2	1E	7	3																✓	✓	✓	–	–	–
BCC	BRANCH ON C=0 (2)																															90	2	2							–	–	–	–	–	–
BCS	BRANCH ON C=1 (2)																															B0	2	2							–	–	–	–	–	–
BEQ	BRANCH ON Z=1 (2)																															F0	2	2							–	–	–	–	–	–
BIT	A∧M				2C	4	3	24	3	2																															M7	✓	–	–	–	M6
BMI	BRANCH ON N=1 (2)																															30	2	2							–	–	–	–	–	–
BNE	BRANCH ON Z=0 (2)																															D0	2	2							–	–	–	–	–	–
BPL	BRANCH ON N=0 (2)																															10	2	2							–	–	–	–	–	–
BRK	(See Fig 1)													00	7	1																									–	–	–	–	–	–
BVC	BRANCH ON V=0 (2)																															50	2	2							–	–	–	–	–	–
BVS	BRANCH ON V=1 (2)																															70	2	2							–	–	–	–	–	–
CLC	0→C													18	2	1																									–	–	0	–	–	–
CLD	0→D													D8	2	1																									–	–	–	–	0	–
CLI	0→I													58	2	1																									–	–	–	0	–	–
CLV	0→V													B8	2	1																									–	–	–	–	–	0
CMP	A-M (1)	C9	2	2	CD	4	3	C5	3	2							C1	6	2	D5	4	2	DD	4	3	D9	4	3	D1	5	2										✓	✓	✓	–	–	–
CPX	X-M	E0	2	2	EC	4	3	E4	3	2																															✓	✓	✓	–	–	–
CPY	Y-M	C0	2	2	CC	4	3	C4	3	2																															✓	✓	✓	–	–	–
DEC	M-1→M				CE	6	3	C6	5	2										D6	6	2	DE	7	3																✓	✓	–	–	–	–
DEX	X-1→X													CA	2	1																									✓	✓	–	–	–	–
DEY	Y-1→Y													88	2	1																									✓	✓	–	–	–	–
EOR	A⊻M→A (1)	49	2	2	4D	4	3	45	3	2							41	6	2	55	4	2	5D	4	3	59	4	3	51	5	2										✓	✓	–	–	–	–
INC	M+1→M				EE	6	3	E6	5	2										F6	6	2	FE	7	3																✓	✓	–	–	–	–
INX	X+1→X													E8	2	1																									✓	✓	–	–	–	–
INY	Y+1→Y													C8	2	1																									✓	✓	–	–	–	–
JMP	JUMP TO NEW LOC.				4C	3	3																												6C	5	3				–	–	–	–	–	–
JSR	(See Fig 2) JUMP SUB				20	6	3																																		–	–	–	–	–	–
LDA	M→A (1)	A9	2	2	AD	4	3	A5	3	2							A1	6	2	B5	4	2	BD	4	3	B9	4	3	B1	5	2										✓	✓	–	–	–	–

MNEMONIC	OPERATION	IMMEDIATE OP	N	#	ABSOLUTE OP	N	#	ZERO PAGE OP	N	#	ACCUM. OP	N	#	IMPLIED OP	N	#	(IND,X) OP	N	#	(IND),Y OP	N	#	Z.PAGE,X OP	N	#	ABS,X OP	N	#	ABS,Y OP	N	#	RELATIVE OP	N	#	INDIRECT OP	N	#	Z.PAGE,Y OP	N	#	N	Z	C	I	D	V
LDX	M → X	(1) A2	2	2	AE	4	3	A6	3	2																BE	4	3							B6	4	2	✓	✓	–	–	–	–
LDY	M → Y	(1) A0	2	2	AC	4	3	A4	3	2													B4	4	2	BC	4	3										✓	✓	–	–	–	–
LSR	0→[ ]→C				4E	6	3	46	5	2	4A	2	1										56	6	2	5E	7	3										0	✓	✓	–	–	–
NOP	NO OPERATION													EA	2	1																						–	–	–	–	–	–
ORA	A V M → A	09	2	2	0D	4	3	05	3	2							01	6	2	11	5	2	15	4	2	1D	4	3	19	4	3							✓	✓	–	–	–	–
PHA	A → Ms S-1 → S													48	3	1																						–	–	–	–	–	–
PHP	P → Ms S-1 → S													08	3	1																						–	–	–	–	–	–
PLA	S+1 → S Ms → A													68	4	1																						✓	✓	–	–	–	–
PLP	S+1 → S Ms → P													28	4	1																						(RESTORED)					
ROL	[ ]				2E	6	3	26	5	2	2A	2	1										36	6	2	3E	7	3										✓	✓	✓	–	–	–
ROR	[ ]				6E	6	3	66	5	2	6A	2	1										76	6	2	7E	7	3										✓	✓	✓	–	–	–
RTI	(See Fig 1) RTRN INT													40	6	1																						(RESTORED)					
RTS	(See Fig 2) RTRN SUB													60	6	1																						–	–	–	–	–	–
SBC	A-M-C̄ → A	(1) E9	2	2	ED	4	3	E5	3	2							E1	6	2	F1	5	2	F5	4	2	FD	4	3	F9	4	3							✓	✓	✓ (3)	–	–	✓
SEC	1 → C													38	2	1																						–	–	1	–	–	–
SED	1 → D													F8	2	1																						–	–	–	–	1	–
SEI	1 → I													78	2	1																						–	–	–	1	–	–
STA	A → M				8D	4	3	85	3	2							81	6	2	91	6	2	95	4	2	9D	5	3	99	5	3							–	–	–	–	–	–
STX	X → M				8E	4	3	86	3	2																									96	4	2	–	–	–	–	–	–
STY	Y → M				8C	4	3	84	3	2													94	4	2													–	–	–	–	–	–
TAX	A → X													AA	2	1																						✓	✓	–	–	–	–
TAY	A → Y													A8	2	1																						✓	✓	–	–	–	–
TSX	S → X													BA	2	1																						✓	✓	–	–	–	–
TXA	X → A													8A	2	1																						✓	✓	–	–	–	–
TXS	X → S													9A	2	1																						–	–	–	–	–	–
TYA	Y → A													98	2	1																						✓	✓	–	–	–	–

(1) ADD 1 TO "N" IF PAGE BOUNDRY IS CROSSED.
(2) ADD 1 TO "N" IF BRANCH OCCURS TO SAME PAGE.
    ADD 2 TO "N" IF BRANCH OCCURS TO DIFFERENT PAGE.
(3) CARRY NOT = BORROW.
(4) IF IN DECIMAL MODE Z FLAG IS INVALID.
    ACCUMULATOR MUST BE CHECKED FOR ZERO RESULT.

X   INDEX X
Y   INDEX Y
A   ACCUMULATOR
M   MEMORY PER EFFECTIVE ADDRESS
Ms MEMORY PER STACK POINTER

+   ADD
–   SUBTRACT
∧   AND
V   OR
∀   EXCLUSIVE OR
✓   MODIFIED
–   NOT MODIFIED
M7 MEMORY BIT 7
M6 MEMORY BIT 6

N   NO. CYCLES
NO. BYTES

Courtesy MOS Technology, Inc.

COMMON CHARACTERISTICS

PROGRAMMING MODEL

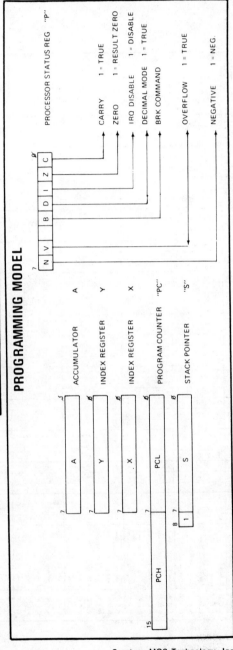

Courtesy MOS Technology, Inc.

Index